DOLPHINS –
SEA
PEOPLE

DOLPHINS—
SEA
PEOPLE

by
Esse Forrester O'Brien

The Naylor Company
Book Publishers of the Southwest
San Antonio, Texas

By The Same Author

ELEPHANT TALES
OUR BABIES
BOTTLE BABIES
ADOPTED BABIES
CLOWNS OF THE FOREST
BARNEY
BAYLOR BEAR MASCOTS
ANIMAL TOTS
REINDEER ROUNDUP
ART AND ARTISTS OF TEXAS
CIRCUS — CINDERS TO SAWDUST
THE FIRST BULLDOGGER

Excerpts from *Man and Dolphin* by John C. Lilly
Copyright ©, 1961 by John C. Lilly. Reprinted by
permission of Doubleday & Company, Inc.

THIS BOOK

IS

AFFECTIONATELY DEDICATED

TO

MY GRANDCHILDREN

JEAN CAWOOD O'BRIEN

AND

ESSE CLAY O'BRIEN

Foreword

ESSE FORRESTER O'BRIEN's DOLPHINS — SEA PEOPLE is
an interesting and well-written book about cetaceans, especially the dolphins or porpoises. From early times these
mammals have attracted world-wide attention in fables and
stories. However, in recent years they have gained wide re-
nown and popularity in the field of entertainment and
science. Because of their high-rated intelligence these fascinating creatures are trained to perform difficult and spectacular tricks to amuse spectators at aquariums around the
world. The dolphins have become so popular as entertainers
that they are now well established in the field of motion
pictures and television. The ability of dolphins, without
hands or feet, to demonstrate such precision, intelligence and
understanding certainly places them in a category above land
animals.

The dolphins are as different, perhaps, as inhabitants of
some other planet. The facts about dolphins are stranger
than fiction. Esse Forrester O'Brien has delved into the
myths and actual facts and writes about them in an interest-

ing style that the layman can understand. However, she has not left out the results of important scientific studies being conducted on an extensive scale. Some of these findings may prove of great benefit to our military services and to the human race. Whether one is old, young, or middle aged this fascinating book will be found most interesting.

I think the dolphin story herein is very well told.

Capt. William B. Gray, Author and
Director of Collections and Exhibits
Miami Seaquarium

Acknowledgments

ESPECIALLY TO Dr. and Mrs. John C. Lilly for letters and help in many ways; Dr. Winthrop N. Kellogg for letters and brochures; Antony Alpers for letters from his publisher, Houghton Mifflin Co., and Alice Bartholomew for letters from the same; also Arthur C. Clarke for letters from his agent, Scott Meredith. Authors Betty and Berm Brothers for their letters and pictures; and author Frederick C. Appel for letters, articles and other help.

To Marineland of Florida and Robert A. Dahne, Director of Public Relations; Captain William B. Gray, director and curator, for letters, pictures and brochures. Marineland of the Pacific and William E. Campeau for letters, pictures and brochures. Sea World, San Diego, California, and Mike Downs for letters, pictures and brochures. Hank Meyer Associates, Florida, and Mr. Bill Kofoed for letters, pictures and brochures. Santini's, Florida, for letters, pictures and brochures.

To Robert L. Edwards, Assistant Laboratory Director of the Interior, Fish and Wild Life; and Robert L. Livingstone

Jr. for letters and brochures. Also Florida Development Commission and Wendell Jarrard for letters, pictures and brochures. Congressman W. R. Poage for letters, sources and U. S. Government brochures; and Mrs. Robert Dadadie for California sources, letters and newspapers.

To the National Geographic Society, letters; *Popular Science*, letters and pictures; *The Saturday Evening Post*, letters, articles and other help.

To Lucy Hill Brewer, librarian of the Waco Public Library, for her hours of patience in tracing material; and L. Pearlstein, reference librarian, Library of Congress, for letters and sources.

Contents

List of Illustrations

xiii

Jack was a Risso's Dolphin (Grampus griseus), a
ecies known to live around the Tasman Sea. He
wn in history as one of the friendliest of all dol-
several reasons: (1) his service to man (2)
iod in which he was known to man (3) his abode
actically the same (4) he was the first dolphin
otection a country ever enacted a law. Many
d authors visited this area of New Zealand just
te about Pelorus Jack; among these were Rud-
Mark Twain, and Frank T. Bullen. Pelorus
well known magazine character in his day.
osed in his honor, and post cards showing
sold throughout the world. He even made
column of his home newspapers when he
ee day holiday.

s, "For more than twenty seven years, from
orus Jack regularly met and accompanied
ssed Cook Strait, between the two main
and, on the run between Wellington and
over a certain stretch of water near the
Sound and nowhere else." This was a
s and very narrow passage of the trip,
ships felt safer with him alongside.

Jack heard a ship's engine, he would
though meeting a dear friend; and
nd frolicking, one would believe he
elf were an old and needed friend.
haste, he would end his rush with a
side of the ship, much to the enjoy-

Page 5   Marineland is the first aquarium to have a porpoise born and live in captivity. COURTESY OF MARINELAND OF FLORIDA.

Page 6   A mother porpoise and a guardian "auntie" futilely raise stillborn calf to the surface for air. COURTESY OF MARINELAND OF FLORIDA.

Page 7   A mother and baby porpoise swim in the waters of the Oceanarium at Marineland of Florida. COURTESY OF STATE OF FLORIDA, DEVELOPMENT COMMISSION — FLORIDA NEWS BUREAU, TALLAHASSEE, FLORIDA.

Page 8   Note the stream of little bubbles coming from the blowhole of the dolphin. COURTESY OF SEA WORLD.

PICTURE SECTION NO. IV   Between pages 80 and 81.

Page 1   Dr. John C. Lilly watches a baby dolphin wrap its tongue around tube, sealing out water. COURTESY OF COMMUNICATION RESEARCH INSTITUTE, Coconut Grove, Miami, Florida — PHOTO BY FRANK S. ESSAPIAN.

Page 2   A scientific investigator swims with a dolphin to become acquainted with this air breathing mammal. COURTESY OF COMMUNICATION RESEARCH INSTITUTE, Coconut Grove, Miami Florida — PHOTO BY FRANK S. ESSAPIAN.

Page 3   Clown laughing with inner tube on snout. COURTESY OF MIAMI SEAQUARIUM.

Page 4   After capture a shark must be "walked" in the aquarium tank to fill his lungs with air. COURTESY OF MARINELAND OF FLORIDA.

Page 5   Carolina Snowball, the world's only known albino dolphin, was captured off the Carolina Coast. COURTESY OF MIAMI SEAQUARIUM — PHOTO BY ANITA REECE CONKLIN.

Page 6   Carolina Snowball, the rare and beautiful albino porpoise, says "hi!" COURTESY OF MIAMI SEAQUARIUM — PHOTO BY ANITA REECE CONKLIN.

Page 7   The blindfolded dolphin proves his excellent sonar system is not related to his vision. REPRINTED COURTESY OF POPULAR SCIENCE MONTHLY (C) 1964 BY POPULAR SCIENCE PUBLISHING CO. INC.

Page 8   The dolphin leaps many feet to receive his reward for a job well done. COURTESY OF MIAMI SEAQUARIUM.

ONE OF ᴛ
story, fo
phin, ᴵ
and d
in or

M
fi
l

XV

"The dolphin is the only creature who loves man for his own sake. Some land animals avoid man altogether and the tame ones such as dogs, horses, elephants are tame because he feeds them. To the dolphin alone, beyond all others, nature has granted what the best philosophers seek; friendship for no advantage. Though it has no need at all for any man, yet it is a genial friend to all, and has helped many."

Plutarch

Pelorus Jack

ONE OF THE OLDEST STORIES — and it should not be called a story, for it is an established fact — is the incident of a dolphin, Pelorus Jack, befriending and caring for man. Facts and dates establish that Pelorus Jack lived twenty-seven years in one locality.

Antony Alpers, in his excellent book, *Dolphins, The Myth and the Mammal,* gives the most interesting and verified account of the illustrious life and work of this famous Pelorus Jack. His life unfolded in the early era of cameras, in the newspapers of the day, and when the telegraph was still young. Since the author and Pelorus Jack were both New Zealanders, it is no wonder that Mr. Alpers' account carries so much feeling and authenticity. Mr. Alpers obtained documented reports from hundreds of people still living in New Zealand who had actually seen Pelorus Jack.

1

Pelorus Jack was a Risso's Dolphin (Grampus griseus), a beakless species known to live around the Tasman Sea. He will go down in history as one of the friendliest of all dolphins for several reasons: (1) his service to man (2) the long period in which he was known to man (3) his abode remained practically the same (4) he was the first dolphin for whose protection a country ever enacted a law. Many celebrities and authors visited this area of New Zealand just to see and write about Pelorus Jack; among these were Rudyard Kipling, Mark Twain, and Frank T. Bullen. Pelorus Jack was also a well known magazine character in his day. Music was composed in his honor, and post cards showing his picture were sold throughout the world. He even made the local social column of his home newspapers when he took a two or three day holiday.

Mr. Alpers says, "For more than twenty seven years, from 1888 onwards, Pelorus Jack regularly met and accompanied the ships that crossed Cook Strait, between the two main islands of New Zealand, on the run between Wellington and Nelson. He did this over a certain stretch of water near the entrance to Pelorus Sound and nowhere else." This was a particularly dangerous and very narrow passage of the trip, and passengers on all ships felt safer with him alongside.

Whenever Pelorus Jack heard a ship's engine, he would come on the gallop as though meeting a dear friend; and from all his leaping and frolicking, one would believe he felt as though he himself were an old and needed friend. Sometimes, in his great haste, he would end his rush with a tremendous splash by the side of the ship, much to the enjoy-

2

ment of the onlookers. In his exuberance he would actually rub against the ship. One correspondent wrote, "He swam alongside in a kind of snuggling-up attitude."

The fame of Pelorus Jack spread great distances and many people made the trip just to see him; and as they crowded the bow of the ship, they were seldom disappointed. He would guide one ship to a certain point and then wait to render his service to one going in the reverse direction. He would always, in his work as a trusted guide, miss the terribly swift current and the dangerous whirlpools by about three-quarters of a mile; and the steamers never hove any closer than that.

Pelorus Jack was between 12 and 14 feet in length, short and heavy in appearance, grey in color, and whitish underneath. His head was thick and rounded, and so he did not resemble other dolphins in this respect. He loved the fast moving steamers; therefore he paid no attention to smaller boats.

Passengers, when nearing the pass, would anxiously scan the horizon; when the call came, "Here comes Pelorus Jack," excitement and pleasure (and to many a feeling of safety) reigned. Captain Ray of one of these ships described him as "a veteran master of the Nelson run."

Seeing Pelorus Jack by night was even more exciting than seeing him by day. Fred Parltrop describes this experience as: "If you can visualize a mass of phosphorescent fire 14 feet in length traveling through the water with the greatest of ease, then suddenly leaping into the air, the spray and dripping water from him giving one the impression of

3

innumerable fine flashes of electricity, you will get some idea of what Jack looked like."

Pelorus Jack drew more and more tourists. In fact, Bill Morrison, who ran an accommodation house near French Pass, had a sign painted on a rock, in huge white lettering: "Pelorus Jack Can Be Seen From The Verandah Of The Boarding House."

Then came a sad day. Someone on one of the steamships fired at Pelorus Jack with a rifle. So far as is known, he was not even hit, but this act led to a demand that Pelorus Jack be protected by law. This request was heeded, but the law was not passed until two years later, reading in part:

Order in Council

At the Government House, at Wellington, this 26th day of September, 1904.

Present:

His Excellency the Governor in Council

and the order presented the regulations.

On March 16, 1912, the Secretary of Marine, George Allport, drew his minister's attention to the need to renew Pelorus Jack's protection for a further three years, and this was done shortly afterwards.

Sometime during the year of 1912, Pelorus Jack was missed, and for the last time. The concluding paragraph in an obituary editorial in the *Marlborough Express* (the newspaper of Pelorus Jack's home district) published on October 28, 1912, reads: "Never before, it is said, has this curious 'pilot' of the French Pass been 'absent from duty' so long, and naturally there exists no little anxiety as to what has become of him. . . .

" 'Jack' has rightly been termed one of the wonders of the world. Many visitors to New Zealand have made him one of the 'sights' to be viewed during their itinerary, and many who at first were sceptical as to the existence of such a creature have gone away convinced. 'Pelorus Jack' is beloved by all seafaring men whose ships he has befriended; his coming formed a pleasant break in the monotony of the daily round of toil. If he is dead, more's the pity; if he has been slaughtered, more's the shame."

Cowboy of the Sea

MR. DOLPHIN! HE IS NOT A FISH! He is an animal and belongs to the animal family just the same as dogs, lions, cows, horses, and others. James Poling said of him, "He looks like a fool, lives like a king, swims like a fish, and thinks like a man."

The dolphin is a member of the whale order and is known as a "toothed whale." Stated in earthly "kin-ology," his ancestral cousins, the whales and the porpoises, first lived in the sea and then became landlubbers, but for some unknown reason deserted the land to return to the sea. All of this happened about sixty million years ago or more. Possibly returning back to the sea was a very wise and far-sighted move. The dolphin seems to have retained for himself the best of two worlds — the land and the sea. There is

7

approximately three hundred times more room for marine life in the sea than for life on the land. Therefore about four-fifths of the world's surface is theirs without boundaries. Most continents are separated from one another (by water) but oceans, seas and bays are connected by water.

Water gives more support to an animal's body, thus allowing it to grow larger than any land animal — even a dinosaur. There is an over-abundance of food — fish of all kinds are their's to choose. There is lots of room for swimming and playing. The dolphins may also choose their climate. Thousands upon thousands of them live in the warm waters of the Gulf Stream which flows into the Gulf of Mexico, around the Florida coast and on up the Eastern coast of the United States. Gradually this stream reaches Northern waters and loses the heat it absorbed from the rays of the sun near the equator.

Dolphins are also found in great numbers off the California Coast and in almost all open seas, but they seem to prefer living close to shore. Perhaps one reason is that their enemy, the killer whale, makes his abode in the deeper, cooler water. Dolphins also go up large rivers as they can easily live in fresh water. All of these fish-like mammals — the dolphins, porpoises, and whales — spend their entire time in the water although they have to breathe air, and in order to do so, they must surface.

The difference between the dolphin and the porpoise is that the dolphin has a snout and the porpoise does not. The porpoise is smaller, more slender and more streamlined. The dolphin is chubby in comparison with the porpoise.

Considering lines of beauty and coloring the common dolphin has a classical appearance — one writer said, "of scholarliness." There is a black ring around each eye and, set against white, this makes him appear to be wearing glasses. The black coloring on his back dips in sharp lines as though he were wearing a saddle or a coat with tails. The underside of his body is almost pure white.

The coloring of the bottle-nosed dolphin is more muted — blended — his color greyish, and the underneath of his body more tannish. The bottle-nosed dolphin is more easily distinguished by the pronounced groove between his eyes and mouth, giving a snub-nose effect. The most pleasing feature in the physical appearance of the bottle-nosed dolphin is the fashion in which his mouth curves upward, giving him quite a happy expression. This expression is called by almost all scientists and admirers of him, "the frozen smile." The bottle-nosed truly lives up to this expression, for he is friendly, content and happy, and has a wonderful disposition. The smile really seems to be a built-in, mischievous smile.

The dolphin's recent claim to fame and acclaim is largely due to the scientific research being done on him. The reason for this intense and increasing scientific interest is most understandable.

There are many good reasons why the scientists are focusing so much research on the dolphin. The anatomy of the dolphin is most ideal for study, as is his disposition.

In fact, this sociable creature has been a friend to man since before the time of Christ. To the early Christians he was a symbol of love, diligence and speed. It is supposed that the first recorded contacts between man and dolphin may be those of Aristotle in the fourth century before Christ. His account of the anatomy and behavior of the dolphin is still fairly accurate.

The early Greek, Roman, and English writers — Plutarch, Pliny, Herodotus, Oppian, Shakespeare and others have written in glowing terms of the dolphin. He has been a favorite of sailors since the first ships went to sea. These early sailors considered him a good omen. Whenever dolphins coursed alongside their vessels they felt that the elements would favor them and that the dolphins were a sign of steady winds and fair weather.

The dolphin with his antics of fun, frolic, and friendliness has attracted the interest of all men. There is no written statement as far back as history goes, or even by word of mouth, of any instance where a dolphin harmed man. On the contrary the dolphin has always been most friendly to man.

Many of the stories of the early Greek and Roman writers, such as Pliny's report of a dolphin carrying a boy to school every day on his back, have been considered fanciful; but in the light of recent research such stories are not only feasible but have present day counterparts. In Marineland of Florida, the Miami Seaquarium, and other oceanariums, dolphins have been trained to work in a harness and pull a surfboard taking a child and a dog for rides or to pull a girl in a small boat.

Probably all of the scientific research and the recordings

of recent findings will be easier to conceive if we consider the physical makeup of the dolphin. Dr. Arthur C. Clarke, speaking through one of his characters in *Dolphin Island* says, "Every dolphin is a person in his own right, an individual with more freedom than we can ever know on land. They don't belong to anyone and I hope they never will. I want to help them, not only for Science, but because it is a privilege to do so. Never think of them as animals; in their language they call themselves People of the Sea and that's the best name for them."

Scientists seem to have developed a love and understanding of the dolphin even before they started their intensive study. As this research continues, it does not seem to be solely on the basis of cold facts, but as a desire for mutual understanding and benefit. And be it said for the dolphin first, last, and for all time, that he is the most co-operative of any subject ever to come under careful research and sustained study.

Research problems have been and are dealing with the dolphin's anatomy, physiology, behavior, communication, sonar, emotions, nervous systems and other life aspects. Marine biology, as a whole, has profited by all these experiments.

In the physical makeup of the dolphin, many points of anatomy go back to the dolphin's days on land. The very core of the research is the comparable size of the brains of man and the dolphin. The dolphin has a large brain; and, in proportion to the length of his body, it is second in size only to the brain of man. That is, for each foot of the length of the body, a dolphin has a little less than seven ounces of brain as compared to about eight and one half ounces of brain to every foot a man measures. To bring this into clearer perspective, the gorilla, which has been termed "our nearest anthropoid cousin," judged on the same basis, has only about three ounces to every foot of his size.

The above measurements mean that a dolphin's brain is one and one-half times as large as man's, because his average weight is around 400 pounds and he is from 8 to 10 feet in length. Thus a large brain with a peaceful temperament and sociable disposition is most desired for scientific experiments.

The fact that the dolphin was a land animal at one time also helps in this experimental work since scientists have done more research on land animals. Of course sixty million years or more have passed since the dolphin left the land. What were, or served as, their front legs or arms while on earth, have become their flippers or paddles. Inside a flipper is a five-toed foot (or a five-fingered hand), also a wrist, forearm (two bones) and an upper arm. The dolphin has very little mobility in any of these joints, except in the case of the ball-like shoulder joint which has a considerable amount of mobility. The flippers, which are controlled by the shoulder muscles, enable the active dolphin to do everything from the "barrel roll" to the "flying maneuvers of the airplane." There is a triangular shaped dorsal fin on the dolphin's back that enables him to execute all his turns and his graceful bankings when in a small pool of shallow water.

After leaving land the dolphins had no need of hind

legs so there remain only two bones which were once his hip bones. He has sixty-four vertebrae. Since hair was not needed in the water — it disappeared. The only sign of hair now is six bristles of stiff hair on each side of the baby dolphin's snout before birth, but these disappear by the time of birth. The mouth has become a beak that contains eighty-eight conical teeth which interlock upper and lower jaws that are excellent for catching fish. A dolphin catches his fish crosswise, switches them lengthwise with his eight inch tongue, and swallows them whole. If he so desired, he could clip them to pieces with his sharp teeth. A dolphin has no grinding teeth as man does. His lower jaw is undershot, with a sort of chin sticking out in front of the upper jaw.

These jaws are tremendously strong as evidenced by their use in butting their enemy the killer whale. These killer whales commit wanton slaughter among dolphins, who will avoid them whenever there is a possible chance. Dolphin live in shallow water where the killer whales cannot swim and this is a great protection. When a killer whale is threatening a herd of dolphins, the old bull dolphin herd leader bravely enters the battle, butting, ramming and attacking with fury. Then all of the dolphins join in, butting the whale around the gills. If they are lucky, they cause bleeding and then they all join in nibbling and biting away his lips.

The dolphin can be a very rough, tough, and persevering fighter. He snaps his jaws like a crocodile and this is no idle sword rattling on his part. He backs up his threats and warnings. Even sharks and whales, with the single exception of the killer whale, know better than to attack him. Using his bonehard snout a dolphin can easily kill a shark by rupturing its vulnerable liver, or kill a whale by breaking its jaws. Fisherman have told of seeing an eight or ten-foot dolphin weighing about two hundred and fifty pounds attack a one thousand pound hammerhead shark. When the chips are down, our otherwise smiling, good natured, co-operative dolphin is a real sea-fighter.

A dolphin has a well developed sense of taste. Every so often you may see a dolphin open his mouth and let the water flow through. Thus he may receive a trace of fish, whale, or varying objects.

His vision is most excellent. It seems that the dolphins are able to see as well in air as in water. A dolphin can catch a small football with his eyes above the water and jump high to make the catch. His eyeballs are about two inches in diameter, and he can look outward, upward, forward, and downward.

The hearing organs of the dolphin and the porpoise are visible only as tiny "pin-holes" on each side of the head, located just back of the eye. However, these ears have a dense, well-developed middle ear structure that enables the dolphin to hear extremely well.

When people watch a herd of dolphins as they roll alongside or race in front of a ship, the general opinion is that there is only the dorsal fin and part of the back out of water. This is not the case. The speedy dolphin, in one roll, lets out through his blowhole, or nose on top of his head, all of the used air from his lungs and takes in enough air to refill his lungs. This enables him to stay under water as long as four to six minutes, although it appears that they surface to breathe about every three minutes.

Observation of sleeping dolphins has been made possible in the great glass tanks of oceanariums and marinelands. The dolphins lie or float about a foot or two below the surface of the water, with their strong tails dangling limp. Their eyes are closed. However, when they need a breath of air every minute or so, seemingly with no effort, their wide tail gives a flip and they rise to the surface. Usually they open, or half-way open their eyes once or twice while taking a breath, but often do not seem to wake at all. A baby dolphin sleeps under its mother's tail, and they both surface to breathe at the same time.

Whenever possible, all members of a dolphin family sleep together. It has been found that keeping families together in the tanks makes them happier. Family life is important, but the herd pattern of the wild dolphins in the open waters is necessary for protection. Here they swim together in close formation with the mothers and their young ones in the center of the formation. Some mariners will vow that they have heard dolphins snore.

Another very important part of a dolphin's make-up is his backbone and tail. He pushes himself forward with his tail; so does a fish, but there are striking differences between the two. The fish and the snake swim by bending their backbones sideways. They flick to the left or right but cannot go up and down as quickly as the dolphin. He bends his back-

15

bone vertically like a "galloping dog," and his tail moves up and down. He can also turn sideways quickly although he may be swimming very fast, because the muscles in a dolphin's caudal penduncle have been built out above and below the spinal column. The dolphin's tail is very helpful in gaining speed in locomotion and his entire body seems to be streamlined for action.

One more comparison between the physical make-up of the fish and the dolphin. A dolphin steers his course with his flippers as well as his tail. A fish uses his fins and his tail. The main difference is that a fish's tail is perpendicular to its body, while a dolphin's tail is crosswise or horizontal to his body. Because of the dolphin's unusual speed — ranging from 12 to 30 miles and hours — he is often called "The Arrow of the Sea."

Taking fish crosswise in mouth.

A bottle-nosed porpoise dozes as it swims beneath water at Marineland of Florida.

The gentle dolphin must sometime defend itself with its blunt snout.

Dolphins teasing pelicans Pete and Repete and waiting to get a feather.

Sharon Conrad takes a porpoise powered ride at Marineland of Florida.

COURTESY OF MIAMI SEAQUARIUM — PHOTO BY ANITA REECE CONKLIN

Little Miss Universe Queen, Renne Crevalle, gives a pat to a Miami Seaquarium dolphin.

Mr. Dolphin—What is his I.Q?

MAN HAD BETTER PUT ALL HIS mental powers on roller skates, or he will no longer be able to remain number one in intelligence on the face of this old earth. Many times the question has been asked: "Just how smart is a dolphin?" The dolphin's almost uncanny ability to learn, the ease with which he solves so many problems just as if "thinking" them through, and his inventiveness in devising games certainly place him in a high mental order. The dolphin also has an excellent memory and recognizes man's signals and sounds.

In the not too distant future we may find that Mr. Dolphin has outdistanced man. The National Geographic Society says that the dolphin is "Gaining recognition as a mental giant of the animal kingdom," and the *Science Digest* reports, "Porpoise rated genius among animals." Dolphins show certain characteristics of human behavior. Each of

17

these remarkable animals has his own personality. Like man, they are social creatures and they act independently of their fellows.

Scientists give a list of attributes by which intelligence may be tested. Listing a few of them, we find that the dolphin qualifies in the matter of solving a problem. One interesting example of this is the case of the playful young dolphin and the feather. When the old pelicans were happily floating along on the pool, this young dolphin prankster would make dashes at them, pulling out a feather but never biting the pelican. This dolphin's name is Algae. He immediately discovered the game of "fetch." He would take the feather down to one of the sea-water jets at the bottom of the pool where the water was swift as it came in, and turn the feather loose. Then he would shoot up to the top of the water and catch it as it came to the surface. He soon interested a dolphin friend of his in this game. Algae was a precocious little fellow and always enjoyed the company of older friends. One would take the feather down, put it in the swift water, turn it loose, and the other would wait and catch it as it came to the top of the water. They would alternate in this routine of "fetching the feather."

Then Algae conceived the idea of throwing the feather out to people who were standing around the pool, and they would throw it back to him. One day the feather stuck high on the side wall of the pool. He could not catch it between his lips and pull it loose because his chin protrudes below the upper lip. The visitors who were watching said Algae paused for just a second, took one quick thought, jumped up and raked the feather loose with the side of his head, and then continued to throw it. This solution showed resourcefulness. Since he enjoyed this game so much, he guarded the feather as his personal property and each day would entice visitors into his game. The feather stuck many times to the side wall, but he always used the same tactics in getting it loose. Thus he had solved a problem on his own initiative and had also shown "sustained interest" (another sign of intelligence) which requires a form of thinking.

This same Algae was always teasing a large red grouper (fish) that lived in a crack in the rocks at the bottom of the pool. Algae would get a piece of squid (a favorite fish of the grouper) and put it near a hole that opened into the crack or cave. Then Algae would back off where the grouper could not see him. As soon as the grouper came out to eat the squid Algae would snatch it away. This is an excellent example of teasing, another test or sign of intelligence. Teasing is action taken "deliberately and anticipating other action." This shows planned action which is indicative of high intelligence.

Such intelligence as this develops from babyhood. Chasing fish, turtles, and other small occupants of the pool is the first mischievous activity of a young dolphin. For example, a dolphin will catch a fish by its tail and pull it backwards, or take it to the surface of the pool and turn it loose. One young dolphin spent much of his time and energy teasing a turtle by pushing it around, tossing it out of the pool with his snout, or rolling it over and over on the bottom of the pool.

19

Dolphins seem to reason things out in a clear-thinking way. This is aided by their great amount of curiosity. At one of the marinelands several stiff street brushes were anchored to the bottom of the pool. In just two or three days the dolphins were scratching themselves, rolling from side to side and on their back. In some of the oceanariums the dolphins become very spoiled and demanding about their food. If one was thrown a dead fish when he was accustomed to a live one, he would throw it "smack" back in the attendant's face.

Priscilla is a well-known performer at Marineland of Florida. She is a natural clown and gives repeat performances just to get more applause and screams of delight from the children. Her pal and partner in this special vaudeville skit of her own making is a turtle, which she picks up, pitches on her nose and balances, no matter how frantic are the efforts of the old turtle to get down. When she has tired of this balancing game, she dumps the turtle off, whereupon, as though collecting for his part in the act, he immediately crawls on her back and she takes him for a ride all around the pool.

A group of dolphins once intercepted a football that veered into the sea. The dolphins merrily batted it with their tails and pitched it back and forth with their snouts, keeping it among themselves swimming off with the new plaything. They evidently crossed the goal line and scored with a "home-swim."

A couple of scientists witnessed a most interesting example of dolphin behavior. Two dolphins were trying to dislodge a moray eel from its rock crevice on the bottom of the pool. One dolphin was on each side and with a seesaw movement was pulling the old eel back and forth in the crevice. Presently one dolphin swam away and soon returned with a dead scorpion fish in his mouth. The scorpion fish has sharp and painfully poisonous dorsal spines. Holding the scorpion in his mouth, the sly dolphin poked the eel with the spines. The eel seemed to jump out of the crevice, whereupon the dolphin caught him, took him to the middle of the tank and up to the surface, and there released him. This is clearly a case on the dolphin's part of thinking ahead and anticipating action on the part of the eel.

All dolphins love to play with inner tubes or plastic rings. They are ideal toys for the dolphin's game of "fetch." Algae learned this inner tube game at six weeks of age. He will throw the ring across the rails of the pool to onlookers who will immediately accommodate him by throwing it back. Two creatures with unlike habits, life, and environment can share in the pleasure of a game; and, when all is said, the dolphin really started the game and taught it to man. If the dolphin tires of the game first, that is perfectly all right; but if an onlooker tires and walks away, he is reprimanded at once and in strong terms. Mr. Dolphin puts his head out of the water and makes a high-pitched, grating noise from his blowhole thus showing his impatience. This is another example of "sustained interest" in wanting to continue the game.

When Algae was only one year of age he had learned to jump out of the water and take a fish from the attendant's mouth. Algae was really a mainspring of activity. By the time he was two years old, two other dolphins had been born in the pool. Algae became the ringleader of the three — a sea version of the Three Musketeers. However, he did not always get away with his pranks as the tooth marks and cuts on his body bore evidence. He was such a good-natured, happy fellow that everybody loved him and, as the expression goes today, he had fun "living it up."

Sometimes as many as three or four dolphins take part in the same game and keep up an excited interest for as long as thirty minutes. Algae, though an adult, still loves to frolic. Most dolphins, like kittens and puppies, lose their interest in frolic and play; however, occasionally youth will return, and a few old fellows will join in a game with the youngsters.

The training of dolphins goes on at a number of marinelands, seaquariums, and oceanariums. They have been taught many stunts. They jump through hoops 10 feet in the air and also through hoops over which paper has been placed. They seem to enjoy the splitting, and tearing sound of the paper. Not to be outdone by circus animals, Splash "the Fearless" jumps through a burning hoop without even drying off. Dolphins have learned to leap 16 to 20 feet in the air to take a fish or other objects held in a man's hand and with the distance of only two or three lengths of his body to get up speed and to know the exact spot to leave the water for his perfect high jump. Many outstanding stunts are taught in these marine schools. One dolphin always rings the school bell and others come trooping in with a book under a flipper. Another dolphin raises the school flag. After receiving instructions from their teacher another dolphin retrieves a dumbbell, splashes water to put out a fire, and tows the school's mascot dog around on a surfboard.

With the dolphin's great amount of energy, intelligence, and curiosity, they are always eager to learn, games seem to hold a special fascination for them. There truly seems to be a spirit of competition. Although they have been taught a number of games, basketball seems to be a general favorite. A university coach was heard to remark that he was thinking of signing up Splash and Sparkle with his team next year. Splash is the star hoopster on the Marineland of Florida basketball team, and Sparkle is the star of the Miami Seaquarium show. Each can be counted upon to make that basket almost everytime he performs in each of their five daily shows. The other dolphins know the game and can make baskets, but Splash and Sparkle are outstanding athletes. Splash and other dolphins take important parts in the skit of a Big League baseball game. If Algae were in this game, one could count on a great deal of arguing with the umpire. When things do not suit him, he rears up out of the water and states his complaints in no uncertain terms.

In listing the stars of Marineland of Florida, it would not be fair to pass by the pilot whale, who is a finished actor. He takes the part of a new student taking the "doctor's" physical examination. He shakes hands and talks to the doctor. Then the huge animal has his heart checked, reflexes tested, and throat examined. Next he has his teeth brushed and shows how he gargles "after every meal." Then he allows his trainer to put his new hat on him. By this time he seems to be in high spirits. Then the whale stands on his head and gives a happy salute to the audience with his tail.

Bubbles is the star of a whale troupe which occupies the circular tank in the main building of Marineland of the Pacific. She goes through five or more performances daily before crowds of fifteen hundred. She is 15 feet long and weighs seventeen hundred pounds. She can sing, dance, shake hands, wave goodbye, lift a plastic "barbell," and jump completely out of the water. She can even leap a hurdle, as do several Pacific striped dolphins. Bubbles is the first whale in the history of civilization captured alive in the open sea expressly for public display.

Bimbo is the largest whale is captivity. He weighs four thousand pounds and is 20 feet in length. In spite of his immense size and weight, he can hurl himself almost completely out of the water to receive a fish from his trainer's hand. Bubbles and Bimbo are both willing performers and have been most co-operative in training.

Dolphins, porpoises, whales and sharks respond readily to good training and actually enjoy showing off their remarkable accomplishments. Their only reward for a feat well done is a piece of fish and the applause of an appreciative audience. They certainly are eager for the applause and show their genuine joy by giving several extra high splashes in the water. Punishment is never used in the training of these animals.

The dolphin is a playboy by nature, yet he can be counted upon to hold his own if he thinks he is being tricked. Once a visitor at a marine exhibition made the mistake of tossing a bony fish head into a tank of dolphins. He got it right back in his face!

Nearly all dolphins love music and can be taught to blow a horn. At Marineland of the Pacific a group of dolphins have been taught to respond by whistling in a siren-like fashion to baton waving and to verbal directions, thus learning to "chorus vocalize" in a singing exercise.

The dolphin's interest in music is not new to the scientists and trainers. Several centuries ago Pliny, author of *Natural History* wrote, "The dolphin is an animal that is not only friendly to mankind but is also a lover of music and it can be charmed by singing in harmony, particularly by the sound of the water organ." The water organ was a musical instrument that was invented by an Egyptian about three centuries before the birth of Christ. It resembled a modern organ very much except that water pressure was used to blow air through the pipes. It could be very loud, so loud that a player had to close his ears. It was used at gladiatorial shows, which were held in the open air. It was also heard at other celebrations on the sea shore. We know now that the short pipes that give the high notes would also have given out ultrasonic vibrations which dolphins hear. It is therefore quite possible that dolphins were attracted by curiosity to the sound of the water organ.

The dolphin is a sociable fellow. It is really uncanny how he wants to shake hands with his flipper at every opportunity, seeming to possess that greeting desire and man-

25

ner of a human. They also love to wave good-bye with their flippers.

The willingness of the dolphin to co-operate is a great help to scientists, especially in judging his intelligence. The fact that he is gregarious also helps in appraising him. We have grown accustomed to the desire on the part of the dog, chimpanzee, horse, elephant and other animals to co-operate with man. On the other hand, the cat does not often show a desire to co-operate; therefore it is difficult to grade a cat's I.Q. One cause for the cat's aloofness is the fact that he lives alone, as a rule, and in the wild state, hunts alone, and so they do not have a leader. Nearly all other animals seem to roam in packs or herds and enjoy a communal life. So it is with the dolphin. There may be a small number in a group or an unbelievable large number in a herd.

Dolphins usually feed and live near the shore yet, in case of an impending storm, hurricane, or tidal wave, the old bull leader of the herd will give a warning signal and all forget their petty grievances, gather in one herd, and retreat to safer, deeper water. The mothers with babies and young dolphins are usually guarded in the center of the herd.

A dolphin can leap or dive with equal grace, executing surface or deep dives with agility. His rolling motion in the water has been called a sort of "land gallop." He can display an extra burst of energy as if he were a propelled rocket, or can crash dive as though setting an example for a submarine. In case of extreme emergency the dolphin can stay under water for ten minutes without surfacing for breath. For this and many other reasons, he is the envy of the skin diver.

LOCKHEED AIRCRAFT CORPORATION

(From an article by Mr. Carl Plain in *The San Diego Union*)

A GREAT AMOUNT OF SCIENTIFIC research and study of the dolphin has been, and is being, conducted by Lockheed California Company, a division of Lockheed Aircraft Corporation. Due to their advanced concepts, such as the Polaris missile, the U-2, A-11, and C-141, the Office of Naval Research is sponsoring this fascinating study of the dolphin. They, as do other research corporations and individual scientists, feel that the dolphin has solved many problems of underwater navigation and that a study of these and other dolphin accomplishments can be of inestimable value to man's search for advanced solutions to many problems so urgently needed in this scientific age in which we are living.

Lockheed has the dolphins close at hand and under ideal conditions for their study. The Lockheed research is near the Marineland of the Pacific, at Palos Verdes, California. And, at San Diego, the dolphins have already moved into their building and pools at Sea World, which, it is claimed, will be the largest oceanarium in the world when completed. Lockheed also maintains its own research ship, the *Sea Quest*, which is stationed at San Diego.

Lockheed's Dr. John J. Dreher, is known as "the man who talks *to* dolphins," and with his evident success, it might be said *with* the dolphins. He has isolated sixty-five separate, individual sounds or dolphinese words. He has recorded six of the thirty-two sounds which he has found

27

that the bottle-nosed dolphins use in their language. He has played these records back to the social breeding colony of dolphins at Marineland and is recording with interest and success, and is analyzing the results. He is very interested in the supersonic range in which dolphins communicate with each other.

Dr. Dreher said, "We tend to measure intelligence by the alacrity (eager readiness) with which an animal can do something we prize." He, like all other scientists, finds the dolphin willing, friendly, and co-operative. He comments, "They're a friendly, nervous animal. They can go off their rocker (rather like a nervous breakdown) especially if they're bedeviled."

One question high on the agenda of all research projects is how the dolphins swim faster than they should, especially considering the amount of energy they expend. Study seems to boil down to the fact that the solution is their skin structure, which produces a laminar, rather than a turbulent, flow.

Although Lockheed research was started as late as 1959, solid progress has been made; there are hopes and promises of answers that will be of practical importance. There are so many areas in which dolphins can teach man. They are able to use oxygen to a degree that no land animal has achieved, even storing it in their muscles. They have solved laminar flow and propulsive forces and thus may be of great help to man in life sciences as well. As an example in this area, "How can a blue whale, (the dolphin's cousin) at a depth of five thousand feet, withstand a pressure of some two tons, on its eyes?" With the ever increasing population, scientists may find a way to build cities on the floor of the ocean and farm the lands down there. The dolphins may then become the farmer boys of future generations and harvest the crops.

Dr. Dreher, like Dr. Lilly, Dr. Kellogg, Dr. Kazan, Dr. Norris, Dr. Scholander and others, feels that if we could only develop mutual communication with the dolphins, practically a whole new world will be open to us. Dr. Dreher, in commenting on this communicative angle said, "It's a long, long road from here to grammar, to a syntax, and a language." He compared the dolphin communication program to efforts at communicating with inhabitants from other planets. He believes it will be possible to train dolphins to find and render aid to underwater swimming teams and to aid mankind in numerous other ways. He gave many confirmed cases of dolphins bearing humans to the surface of the ocean where they could breathe.

Dr. Dreher made a strong observation of the sentimental and emotional side of a dolphin's nature: "Dolphins can become emotionally attached to people and, separated from a favorite trainer, they have been known to go into shock, refuse to work or eat and finally die."

Fisherman's Helper

DOLPHINS ARE OFTEN SEEN RIDING just in front of the bow of a ship with no visible motion of their bodies or effort on their part. In this way they get a free ride from the bow wave, which is the water pushed forward by the bulk of the ship. To an observer, they seem to be coasting.

Many scientific studies have been made of this effortless travel or hitchhiking by the wily old dolphin. It is known that he swims with his tail at about 28⁰ angle to the ship's bow waves to get the full forward thrust. However, not all scientists can agree on the position or angle of the dolphin's body. Dr. P. F. Scholander, a famous scientist, after making an exhaustive study on the subject remarked, "These rascals are a graveyard to our wits. Again we must bow to the dolphin."

Scientists agree that the longevity of the dolphin — about

thirty to forty years is a great aid to their study. This gives scientists time to try and solve the dolphins' mysteries of body, mind, and communication.

It has been found that dolphins can swim at an accelerated speed much longer than fish can, probably because they have an extra supply of oxygen in the cells of their muscles. This fact may help him in his fishing, as the dolphin is known to be an adept fisherman. The early Greek and Roman writers praised his willingness and desire to help man fish. In those early days man depended a great deal on fish for his livelihood. Man came to know the dolphin's method of fishing and learned a manner of diverting the talents of the dolphin; however, man did not outwit the dolphin. The dolphin soon found he could use man in his own fishing plans. If the fishermen could trap a school of fish between their nets and a herd of dolphins there was a better chance of a successful haul. The dolphins, acting as a herd, would drive the fish into the nets. We are told by Pliny that this mutual fishing became a regular plan on the south coast of France, and that the resultant catches were very large.

Pliny said the fishermen and dolphins had formed a fishing partnership, so to speak. With nets filled to capacity (although many mullets jumped over the nets and were eaten by the dolphins) the thoughtful fishermen threw many fish to the dolphins as their share of the catch. The story goes that the next day the dolphins were always given a feast of bread dipped in wine, and that they eagerly awaited this banquet.

32

Corky the porpoise leaps gracefully through a hoop at the Miami Seaquarium.

Bimbo, the biggest whale in captivity, can hurl his body almost completely out of water.

Oppian tells us that near Athens, Greece, fishermen used flaming torches in their fishing. The fish were attracted to the lights, and the smart dolphins soon learned this; perhaps they were also a little curious about the lights. Thus the dolphins would drive the fish toward the fishermen who either netted them or used the trident on the larger ones.

This same technique is used today very successfully in fishing for garfish. It is to the dolphin's credit that they have always been considerate of the men in these fishing expeditions. They postpone their own dinner from the prize catch until victory is assured for the men. It is told that in Asia "suits are not infrequently brought into the native courts to recover a share in a catch of fish in which plaintiff's dolphins have been held to have filled the nets of rival fishermen."

Fishermen have usually been generous in throwing a share of the catch to the waiting dolphins. They believe if they sin against the dolphins they will no longer help them with their fishing. Some old stories tell that not all men were so friendly to the dolphins. The Turks and Thracians feasted on slices of dolphin meat and put the blubber in jars to be used as oil.

Aristotle reports that some of these Greek fishermen niched the tails of the dolphins so they could find out if the same ones came each time and also to ascertain how long a dolphin lived. By this experiment some were known to have lived thirty years. Aristotle was fairly accurate in his reports of twenty-three centuries ago.

It has been suggested, and this is not so far astray in

33

thought, that fishermen should breed and train dolphins, keeping them in compounds and turning them out for the run. Antony Alpers stated in his book, *Dolphins, The Myth and The Mammal* (page 170), "but no amount of atomic fuel and skilled design and man-made sonar would ever be able to compete in such a business with the dolphin, the most superbly equipped of all animals that ever chased fish in the sea."

Dolphins, when fishing for themselves, usually work in a herd. They make a two-thirds circle around a school of fish and driving it into shallow water, surround it. Then each dolphin takes his turn in catching a few for himself.

If we could ever communicate with the dolphins the "science and industry of fishing may be entirely revised." It may prove a great humanitarian step because six million or more hungry people of the world could be fed. No human is as efficient at hunting, tracking, and catching fish as the dolphin. This almost uncanny ability of the dolphin has given him the name of "Cowboy of the Sea."

PAL IN YOUR POOL

Dolphins have grown in popularity not only among scientists, but with laymen as well. It is considered a "status symbol" to have a pet dolphin. It is quite stylish to swim in your own pool with a pet dolphin as your pal. They have taken the place of poodles, leopards, monkeys, and in some instances, falcons.

The cause of this sudden rise in popularity of the dolphins

is, of course, the great amount of scientific interest in them. Also, the dolphin's popularity with the layman is due a great deal to his wonderful disposition and his high I.Q.

The incredible, interesting, and lovable dolphin is called by many the "Clown of the Sea," and with good reasons. He is a playboy at heart when he is not just loafing. He spends his time feasting, playing practical jokes, frolicking with his companions, and making love. Living this care-free life is one reason for his enjoying longevity.

The dolphin really looks like a buffoon with his rolypoly body, twinkling eyes, prodigious protruding nose, and his mouth forever in a broad grin. Sometimes he even makes a game of dining — swimming into a school of mullet and tossing the fish aloft with his beak, then catching them in his mouth.

The playfulness and ability of dolphins and porpoises to learn new things led Marineland of Florida to begin experiments on the animal's intelligence. This resulted in the world's first superbly trained aquatic dolphin stars, Flippy and Splash.

The adolescent dolphin or porpoise matures at about four or five years; thus he enjoys quite a long period of youthful zest, energy and frolic.

Mr. Milton Santini has made a business of capturing dolphins for scientific institutions, oceanariums, seaquariums, and marinelands. The demand has increased so much that Mr. Santini now has a boarding school for dolphins. He captures, trains, and on request boards them. His charge for a dolphin is around $300. His charge for boarding a dolphin, single pen, is $35 monthly, or in a double pen $30 each. An energetic young dolphin will eat sixteen to twenty pounds of mullet a day. The mullet diet is varied with a few other kinds of fish. The dolphin also has the benefit of training if left in this boarding school.

Mr. Santini's best known pupil is Mitzi, a 7 foot, 6 inch, three-hundred pound moving picture star who attained fame and stardom in the M.G.M. production, *Flipper*. This show has attracted wide attention and interest. So successful and pleasing were the box office receipts from *Flipper* that M.G.M. has planned a sequel and also a color television series which was released in the fall of 1964 on N.B.C.

One of the most enthusiastic dolphin owners is Hugh Downs, the TV personality on the *Today* show. He has his own dolphin named DeeDee with whom he frolics and swims. He first became interested in dolphins when he did a *Today* show at Santini's.

Betty and Berm Brothers, artists and authors, are dolphin enthusiasts. Betty and her dolphin, Dal, swim in their lagoon-like pool where each obeys the commands of the other. When Dal calls, "Hup," Betty holds on to his fin for she knows that means they are going to jump. When Dal calls, "Peeeeep," that means "follow me," and they go for a swift swim. Dal is always cautious that he does not swim too near the rock sides of the pool and scratch Betty. When Betty calls, "Down! Down!," and points downward, they immediately go into a swift dive. Dal squeaks for joy when he sees Betty coming to the pool and squeaks in a sad, plaintive tone for her to return when she leaves the pool.

36

Aqua star, Zale Parry (Mrs. Biven), her little three year old daughter, Margaret Biven, and Smiley, their dolphin pal, are all motion picture and TV stars. Two of this trio hold world records and the third, little Margaret, is well on the way to joining these celebrity performers. You might say she is walking in her mother's "flippers," or foot steps.

Zale has appeared in numerous movies and television shows, including several hour-long TV spectaculars emanating from Marineland of the Pacific. She held the world record for deep sea diving both in the free dive and in a decompression chamber — both controlled experiments.

Little Margaret has been swimming since she was two years of age. She and Smiley are the same age and are devoted friends. They are really swimming companions, and Smiley shows she is pleased beyond words (whistles) whenever little Margaret is with her. Smiley is the only dolphin in the world that will dry dock herself on command — just popping out of the water to be loved and petted by Margaret.

When fishermen get together there are usually tall tales exchanged; when race horse owners gather, their's are really fast tales; when cowboys have gab-feasts at roundups and rodeos, each one has had an almost human experience with his Quarter Horse; but when scientists get together, they just wonder and prophesy concerning the fantastic realms of intelligence that dolphins may reach.

Scientist Dr. John C. Lilly, who is studying dolphins, has suggested ways in which dolphins might co-operate with man. They could rescue survivors from shipwrecks, help in extendings man's knowledge of the ocean, they can tell

of creatures of the deep (if they learn to converse with man)
and may settle the mystery of the "Great Sea Serpent."
Dr. Lilly thinks all of these things could be possible if we
can learn to communicate with the dolphin.

Another of Dr. Clarke's characters suggested a long term
project of teaching dolphins to write or draw. Then they
could sign contracts with man, write the history of the sea,
sing the folklore of the sea, and tell stories of the times before man was on earth.

MARINELAND OF THE PACIFIC

AT THE MARINELAND OF THE PACIFIC a Whale and Dolphin
College is conducted. This educational center is housed in
a series of six tanks. Here the dolphins, whales, and other
aquatic stars are trained from the time of their capture until they are sufficiently educated to perform tricks depend-
ably in Marineland's various shows.

Here at Marineland of the Pacific may be seen four different specie of the dolphin — the bottle-nosed dolphin, the
common, the Pacific striped dolphin, and the porpoise. Several months are usually required to teach a dolphin to jump
through a paper-covered hoop and only a few weeks to teach
him to retrieve a rubber baton. As to the time required to
train these co-operative animals, much depends on the in-

dividual's ability to learn and on the trick which they are being trained to do.

The dolphins can always be depended upon to put on a good, fast show. They thoroughly enjoy games — baseball, football, and, as has been said, basketball seems to be their favorite sport. However, they get a lot of pleasure out of bowling and water polo. They always get very excited when putting out fires and racing across the tank tossing life rings with their beaks. There are some members of this dolphin groupe which seem very musical and enjoy singing, tooting horns, and playing drums. Another stunt of vaudeville significance is their hauling small boats with real dogs at the helm. While the majority of the human race communicates by phonetics or the use of words, certain primitive peoples use a language surprisingly similar to the dolphins. Both the Bushmen of Africa and certain tribes of South American Indians use whistles and clicks to communicate. Fantastic though it may seem, researchers in this fascinating field have learned that the vocabulary of the bottle-nose dolphin is considerably more complicated than the language used by three tribes of primitive Mexican Indians.

Mother and Baby

A DOLPHIN MOTHER GIVES BIRTH to one baby at a time — born alive — about twelve months after mating. It is born in rather deep water; and since it must have air immediately, nature planned its entrance into the world tail first, instead of head first as most animals are born. It would drown if it came head first. However, there has been one head first delivery at Marineland, Florida and this little one survived.

The baby dolphin is far more self-reliant than most babies. Normally the new baby surfaces immediately to breathe; but if it does not, the mother dives under it and pushes it up. Thirty minutes after its birth the hungry little one is ready to nurse. The baby does not suck the milk, as the milk is projected into its mouth by a contraction of the mother's muscles. It gets one gulp at a time and surfaces for breath every five seconds and then comes back for another gulp. A dolphin's milk is high in protein and fat.

41

During its very young life it takes advantage of these nursing periods once every hour. At birth the baby is about three feet in length and weighs approximately twenty-five pounds. It can see, swim, and hear at birth but does not have any teeth until it is about two weeks old. It swims by its mother's side or slightly above her at a rather rapid pace, though at first it is wobbly. By the time it is six or seven months of age it eats some squid and other fish, but gets most of its nourishment from its mother's milk until it is about eighteen months.

The behaviour of the expectant dolphin mother is most interesting. It is different from other females in the marineland tank. The last six months of her pregnancy she spends more time to herself, or with just one other female dolphin whom she has chosen as a companion (often another expectant dolphin). They have also been known to choose their own mother as companion and assistant in birth. This companion reminds one of a helpful "auntie." She stands guard during the birth of the baby and then accompanies the mother and calf for weeks afterward. In fact, this friendship between mother dolphin and her helper may continue for a lifetime.

The first successful birth of a dolphin in captivity took place at Marineland of Florida in 1947. Since that time the colony has averaged one birth a year. Marineland of Florida is the only place in the world to exhibit three generations of dolphins living in captivity at the same time.

The time consumed in delivery of a baby dolphin varies from thirty minutes to two hours. Its birth is of great con-

42

cern to the whole herd. All of the dolphins gather around the mother that they may keep away the sharks and guard her from all harm. Of course the "auntie" is always nearby from the very minute of the baby's birth. If the mother does not push the baby up for air, the "auntie" immediately takes over and sees that the little one breathes and is ready to protect it and fight for it at all times. The baby looks exactly like a miniature dolphin. Very soon after birth it recognizes its mother's call and it answers with its babyish whistle or grunt, thus talking, as it were, with its mother. The mother guards her baby very closely. As it gets older she allows it more freedom, but keeps close watch over it until it is about eighteen months old. By then it has quit nursing and is eating fish. Dolphins eat several kinds of fish, among these, mullet, herring, butterfish, spot, and squid which seems to be one of their favorite foods. It has been said that a full grown, energetic dolphin will eat about eighteen to twenty pounds of fish a day.

Mother and baby dolphins are very affectionate. One has never been seen to strike her child, although baby dolphins can be very mischievous and disturbing to their mothers. Their chief entertainment is chasing other baby dolphins, pulling the tails of small fish — just pulling them backwards a short distance and then letting them go — or pestering a small turtle by rolling him over and over and over. They learn very young to hold water in their mouths and spray it at onlookers around the pool. They are also very quick to find out that they can come up under water fowl, frightening them into flight. One writer tells us that these youngsters

43

seem to get into all their mischief while their mothers are trying to take naps. But these babies are not as grown up as they seem to think they are. If one becomes separated from its mother, it whistles continuously until it hears its mother's call and rushes to her.

When baby dolphins die, their mothers have been known to carry their lifeless bodies on their backs for as long as four days. One mother was seen trying to lift her dead baby to the surface grasped between her flippers. A Coast Guard Patrolman tells of a young dolphin being shot as it fed near a New Jersey coast. As the Patrolman was towing the body to sea, two grown dolphins swam, one on each side of the dead one — probably the mother and father or "auntie" — and tried to give balance and assistance. Captain William Gray of the Miami Seaquarium of Florida tells of his party heading south on Biscayne Bay one day, and watching a dolphin continually pushing a dead baby dolphin to the surface. They watched for a long time, proceeded on their trip, and came back the same way two hours later. With a mother's instinct and love, she was still pushing her dead baby to the surface, vainly hoping it would breathe and live.

Not only is diligence, affection, love, and concern shown between mother and baby dolphin, but there are also many other examples of emotion among grown dolphins. They care for their afflicted or wounded and show a profound capacity for grief, even to the point of doing without food and dying by degrees.

Feelings of grief and emotion are felt by man and the higher animals. Man forms close friendships, as do dogs,

44

horses, chimpanzees, elephants and others. Dolphins experience all these emotions. When a mate or lifelong friend dies a dolphin definitely shows sadness. If the dead one is near, the grieved dolphin will circle the body many, many times making a soft whistle; or it may, as has been said, refuse food and die. Since feelings and emotions show a high degree of intelligence, the dolphin is surely up in that hierarchy.

An explosion underwater occurred near a herd of about twenty-four dolphins. One was stunned and it began to swim rapidly around a nearby ship at a 45⁰ degree list. Two of his herd swam up immediately from below, each putting his head under the injured one's to keep him afloat so he could breathe. This pair was relieved by another pair whenever it was necessary for them to surface for breath. The entire herd remained nearby until the stunned one recovered, then the rest of the herd swam off. No herd will desert an injured companion until they see aid is given.

Sailors consider dolphins good omens when they course alongside sailing vessels. For many centuries the sailors have believed that dolphins would save them in case of shipwreck and that they will protect them from man-eating sharks. An interesting modern story, of this protective care by the dolphin occurred during World War II. After regaining consciousness, a sailor found himself being pushed toward shore by a group of dolphins. How he wished he could communicate with them because they were pushing him, (and insisted on completing the mission), toward the shores of the enemy.

Dolphinese

THE GOVERNMENT believes that the dolphin possesses special capacities and characteristics which can serve as an excellent experimental tool for answering pressing and urgent scientific questions. Many university departments of zoology and psychoanalysis, along with interested individual scientists, are giving serious study to the dolphin.

It is believed that the analysis of the high frequency code system of the dolphins will help immeasureably in the transmission of large amounts of information during short periods of time over vast distances of space. The benefits to be derived from this would be tremendous in times of war or emergency.

A great deal of study is being given the sleep patterns of dolphins. It is known that in a condition of weightlessness, as the dolphin is in water, and as our astronauts are in outer-space, that far less sleep is needed than on earth. Man needs more sleep and in long periods because here on earth he has to continually fight or resist the force of gravity. The accumulative sleep time of a dolphin for a day is about two hours — all that is needed. Our men, traveling in outer space, have said they slept about two hours out of every twenty-four and these two hours were made up of short naps instead of long stretches of sleep. Weightlessness is a result of freeing the body from the force of gravity. At present all these experiments are at "the cutting edge of knowledge."

Dr. John C. Lilly, founder and director of Communication Research Institute, Cocoanut Grove, Florida, was the first scientist to seriously attempt communication with the dolphins. He is doing intensive research and is making a special study of the brain of the dolphin. A dolphin's brain looks very much like two boxing gloves placed side by side, palms down. Dr. Lilly hopes that some day he will be able to understand "Dolphinese," the language of the dolphin; and in fact, he has made noteworthy success along this course. He also thinks that the dolphins may be able to understand us.

As has been stated before, the dolphin, above all other animals, has more research possibilities since his brain compares favorably with man's. He is not too large; at one time he lived on land; he seems most eager to learn; possesses a great amount of curiosity; has a marvelous disposition; a peaceable nature; and is more co-operative with man than any other animal.

48

Marineland is the first aquarium to have a porpoise born and live in captivity.

A mother and baby porpoise swim in the waters of the Oceanarium at Marineland of Florida.

Note the stream of little bubbles coming from the blowhole of the dolphin.

Dr. Lilly realizes that "because we are treading very close to the edge of the unknown, we must necessarily be tentative and suggestive rather than definite." He is a cognizant of the fact that we are entering a space age. If our astronauts are to converse with inhabitants of other planets, or non-earthlings, the dolphin is ideal for experiments along these lines. The dolphin has a complex nervous system and a seemingly highly developed language of his own. Of course, having a language of his own could help or deter his success in learning man's language. The odds are that it will help.

In the dolphin's own language they have thirty different clicks, and they also make use of barks, moans, groans, grunts, blasts, jaw claps, and quacks (maybe one reason they are so successful in mimicking Donald Duck.) It has been noted that when they clap their jaws they are annoyed, maybe even angry.

Dr. Lilly has identified, so to speak, several of these dolphin sounds. He has captured on tape one which is an S O S, or very high pitched distress call. It is used by the dolphin when he needs help or is injured. Not only is this call answered by his fellow dolphins, but they will rush to the place from which the S O S was sent. It has also been observed that animals belonging to entirely different species respond to this call, which may very well be an international dolphin S O S.

Dr. Lilly has experimented in several ways with this S O S tape. When he played it to dolphins, they rushed to the scene in search of their friend who needed help. After a very short time he played the tape again, and the dolphins paid no attention. They realized that this was a phony call. As the old saying goes with man, "You can't hollo 'wolf' too often,"; just so, the dolphins were not to be fooled. When dolphins are playing or cruising in a group and something strange excites them, they all start whistling and this enables them to keep together as a herd. The dolphin's ability to hear and to vocalize in ultrasonic sounds is a great help to him in navigation and communication.

Many dolphin sounds cannot be heard by the human ear as they are too high-pitched. But the smart old dolphin has solved this for himself, at least in a self-rewarding way, thus showing how intelligent he is in figuring out a solution, or in putting two and two together. The dolphin is asked to whistle by his trainer; and when he does, he immediately receives a reward. However, the whistle becomes a little higher and higher pitched until the trainer cannot hear him and quits the rewarding. The dolphin quickly drops back in tone so his whistles can be heard in order to get the reward. He thus learns how to stay in man's acoustic range. He had learned the hearing range and stayed within it for the next few hours. "It is experiences like this that give us hope that these animals will attempt to meet us at least halfway in our attempt to communicate with them," Dr. Lilly remarked.

Due to high-pitched sounds, constant use is made of tape and underwater electronic equipment. Dolphins definitely show when they are excited, pleased or sad. Dr. Lilly has noticed that his dolphins sometime mimic what they hear, at first in primitive manner, later becoming more intelligible. This would, in a fashion, seem that the dolphin is trying to say what man says. One of Dr. Lilly's dolphins mimics, very near to perfection, the southern drawl of one of his attendants from Georgia. Their mimicry almost "sounds eerie at times, even using subtle inflections."

Elvar, Dr. Lilly's most promising pupil, was 6 feet and 7 inches and weighed only about 150 pounds when he was bought. Elvar was put in a pool with no other dolphins. Several trainers swam around in the pool with him. He was given balls and other floating toys with which he could play and amuse himself. He was willing to approach people and fraternize with humans within the first week. At times tape recordings of human voices were fed to him. No other audible sounds were allowed to come his way. Soon he started vocalizing because he had been acoustically deprived. He was eager for the stillness to be broken and he enjoyed the human voice.

Elvar developed a great deal of self confidence, was eager to play, even to tease the trainers. He started retrieving objects so the attendants would throw them again. He also began propelling the front part of his body out of the water so he could look all around. He learned to do the "barrel roll" in his trainer's arms, and then escape. He always looked as though he enjoyed being master of that situation.

The walls of Elvar's pool were very smooth, and, although the water was shallow, he could bank as beautifully and as gracefully as an airplane. After he had heard human language for several weeks, his volcalizing became less "dolphinese" and more human — a sort of "Donald Duck" quack.

However he continued to use his sonar creaking-door sound whenever any new object was placed in his pool.

A loud speaker was placed in Elvar's pool direct from our laboratory so he could hear all of the conversations. He soon tried a number game, whistling one, two, three, four or five whistles. If the men whistled these groups back to him he stopped to listen. Then he would give a plaintive call, the "attention" call he gave whenever he desired their company.

Dr. Lilly is very cautious about his findings or predications. He says speculation is useful, but facts must be found to prove it. He continually reminds himself that he is treading on the edge of the unknown.

When we consider the primitive beginnings of our own languages, we find there are cries of distress, fear, hunger, pain, and mating calls and others. A human mother can always correctly interpret the cries of her baby. One reason for this is close and constant contact of a mother with her baby. As in the case of Elvar, one way of making a dolphin vocalize is isolating him from other dolphins. Then with close and constant companionship with a man he will learn to vocalize in an effort to express his needs and wants in a primitive language of his own. If he is rewarded with food or sympathetic talk, then his anxiety is overcome and he is willing to try again. He has learned the rewarding situation. His loneliness is overcome by his human trainer's conversation and a sort of desired company. Man may enjoy solitude at times but not when it reaches the point of lone-

52

liness. Neither does the dolphin enjoy loneliness as he has clearly demonstrated.

A dolphin's skin is very sensitive, and when he is touched and stroked easily, he loses the fear of human contact. A dolphin should never be petted or rubbed around the blow-hole or lips, or any pressure brought upon his larynx, as these places are much too sensitive to be touched. He will struggle to protect himself but never injure man.

Of course, all of Dr. Lilly's experiments are not directly in the communication area, for he draws conclusions from the behavior, the games, reactions to different conditions, emotions, — in other words, all proof of intelligence, or understanding, and habits of the dolphin help him in this great, scientific undertaking with his pupils.

Each dolphin's voice differs very much from another dolphin's voice. For example, some animals fill in between emissions with low frequency whistling, somewhat the same way some people say "ahh" between words. However, the dolphin has at least two separately controllable sonic emitters, one for producing clicks and one for whistles.

In solitude the dolphin's vocal behavior is different from that when in pairs. There is a special phenomenon when a pair will whistle simultaneously, matching frequencies and time patterns. It has been satisfactorily proved that the dolphin has precise and accurate control of his vocalizations or emissions. Trainers who have been with their dolphin pupils for some time soon learn the voice of each, for there is an identifiable difference.

Some day it may be possible to carry on these communication experiments out at sea, where the dolphin will act and "talk" in its natural habitat without the frustrations of captivity — if there are any frustrations; and there surely must be some problems of adjustment.

If a person does not watch out, Elvar fills his mouth with water and will squirt it all over visitors or trainers. One trainer called, "Stop it" and hit the side of Elvar's tank. Elvar seemed to try to mimic, in a way. The trainer repeated "stop it" five times, slapping the side of his tank each time. A tape was being made of this little episode. When slowed down, there was a very definite, "stop it," pronounced by Elvar. The precocious Elvar had learned the word "squirt" and then Dr. Lilly and the trainers worked on two words together, "squirt water." Elvar at first said "wa" separately from "ter" and then after numerous times he came out with a fairly clear, "water." The next project was to teach Elvar to say "squirt water" and then to immediately do so, thereby learning to connect the words with the action. This Elvar learned and put into practice in record time, much to the discomfort of anyone who goes near his pool. Rainwear is quite the dress now around Elvar's pool, and the mischievous one really seems to enjoy this act.

The sound that will make a dolphin come the quickest is the splash of a fish on the water. That is the nearest sound to a school of mullet playing in the water, hence the food reward is very easily accomplished.

All scientists studying the dolphin have learned that punishment methods do not work well, but that rewarding experiences do. Dr. Lilly thinks it necessary, in gaining best results, to use a great deal of variety in the training program. In order not to disturb or tire his dolphins he uses three to five stunts or examinations in rather rapid succession. This also holds the attention of the dolphin pupil — and the pupil watches the trainer as closely, or maybe more so, than the trainer watches him. The dolphin is so intent on learning that he allows no distraction. This also develops a close relationship, companionship, and love between the teacher and the pupil.

It is almost impossible for man to talk under water, (although inventions for this are being worked out); since the transmission of sound from water to air is very weak, and although the dolphins always talk with each other under water, the dolphin will put his head out of water to vocalize in order that he might accommodate man. A chain of communication between dolphin under water and man out of water must be made possible by electronics or other means before two-way conversations will be enjoyed by both.

Dr. Lilly realizes that, "One works continuously at the edge of mystery, when doing research on the frontiers of science." He says, "The basic processes are challenging, at times discouraging, but never boring." Dolphins had become so newsworthy that the editor of The New York *Herald Tribune* allowed one of their editors, also a friend of Dr. Lilly's, Mr. Earl Ubell, to make a trip to St. Thomas. Mr. Ubell extended his news-gathering stay to one of actual labor as a foreman in directing some of the work. The climate, currents of water, and location selected were ideal. A dolphin thrives best in 80^0 to 82^0 water, and this temperature is also comfortable for man to swim with the dolphins.

Dr. Lilly tells that additional help on his project did come from an "unexpected quarter." In 1959 he married Elisabeth Bjerg who had lived in the Virgin Islands the first eight years of her life. Her grandfather was the royal Danish Customs Collector at Frederiksted on the Island of St. Croix before the Islands were bought by the Americans in 1917. Elisabeth has given devoted and unstinted help in all the affairs of the Institute, from helping build plastic and foam rubber crates to doctoring sick dolphins. Dr. Lilly says of her, "She is a remarkable person who devotes herself to the raising of three children and running the Institute office and is still cheerful, gracious, and beautiful. She also has a high sense of adventure and will undertake extremely difficult assignments."

There is general and widespread interest in the dolphin from government sources to the individual. There is a great amount of enthusiasm among the trainers of these co-operative friends of man. "After you've worked with porpoises," one professional trainer remarked, "chimpanzees, dogs, horses, and elephants seem as dull as white mice."

Dr. Lilly does not minimize the difficulties of human communication with the dolphin either in their own language or in English. They live in a different universe. He says, "Compared with me a dolphin is a genius in water, but he would be a moron in the Library of Congress."

Built-in Sonar

THE MARINELANDS, seaquariums, and oceanariums are a boon to all research work being done on the dolphins and marine life. The great glass tanks provide around-the-clock observation for dedicated scientists and interested laymen.

"We live in a world of sights and sounds." Many scientists are doing extensive research on the sounds made by the dolphins, not only for communication purposes, but because the dolphin's radar and also sonar, or echo-location, systems are far superior to man's. There are two electronic inventions which make use of these — the radar that sends out radio waves and is used on land, and sonar, which is used under water where radio waves do not work. Both have become almost precision instruments, but the dolphin still has the better radar and sonar systems.

Sonar was first discovered to be the science used by bats

and shrews when "seeing" with their ears. A blind man orients or gets his location and bearings by the tapping noise of his cane.

Aside from the communicative or "language" sounds made by dolphins, they have a separate and complex "repertoire" — sounds of a special nature which they use to locate fish or any object in the water even though that object makes no sound of its own. It is the dolphin's uncanny ability to locate these objects which do not give out any sound that the scientists are studying for the Navy.

Probably the most extensive study of the sonar system of the dolphin has been conducted by Dr. Winthrop N. Kellogg of Florida State University, Tallahassee, Florida. Dr. Kellogg says the study of the dolphin "is an adventure of excitement and discovery, involving one of the most unusual and intelligent of all animals," and "anyone who has not become personally acquainted with this fascinating animal is missing something really fine. We scientists who have been studying how this remarkable animal navigates without the use of vision, smell, taste, or touch, found ourselves becoming skin and helmet divers. It has been a lot of fun trying to answer the question of how dolphins 'see with their ears'. We have come up with evidence showing the workings of their echo-ranging or sonar system."

The United States Navy has become vastly interested in the sonar system of the dolphin. Dr. Kellogg makes the firm statement, "What these animals can do has a definite bearing on our national defense, as a means of improving manmade sonar."

Dr. Kellogg's research program has extended over twelve years and has included both wild, or free-swimming, as well as captive dolphins. He says, "We have been privileged to become acquainted with one of the most fascinating of living creatures — an intelligent and fun-loving animal which has too long escaped scientific attention. Its playfulness and friendliness with man are no less than phenomenal."

Two dolphins from Marine Studios, Albert and Betty, were placed in a pool, and for six years intensive study and training of them was undertaken by Dr. Kellogg. The pool had a mud bottom which gave forth no echoes. The water was kept stirred and muddy. Experiments were conducted on dark nights, without even moonlight. A screen was placed in such a location as to obscure the scientist's hands.

If a single B B shot were dropped into the pool the dolphins gave forth with creaking noises which soon subsided. However, if a fish were put in the water with a splash, the dolphins lost no time in rushing for the fish, using the creaking sounds and moving their heads from side to side as they neared the fish. The moving of the head from side to side is their way of pin-pointing a target. Albert proved to be the smarter of the two dolphins. He kept a close watch, as if of ownership, over the pool, especially so at feeding time.

For one of Dr. Kellogg's experiments, he had thirty-six metal poles lowered from overhead into the pool. These were put 8 feet apart and the pattern could be changed at will. When the dolphins found the poles in their pool they swam faster, as they always do when excited. Preparations were made so that the slightest sounds underwater were recorded on tape. They bumped into or scraped the poles a few times in the first twenty minutes of this trial session, but no more even with many, many changes in the pole pattern. It looked as though these collisions were caused by the protruding tail flukes after the body of the animal had passed through the opening. However, the intelligent dolphins quickly corrected these errors by navigating with more efficiency.

A food test was made by Dr. Kellogg. Dolphins prefer spot fish to mullet. A 12 inch mullet and a 6 inch spot were lowered into the murky water. Albert made only four mistakes in his first sixteen trials and none in the following one hundred and forty trials — getting the spot each time. Then a piece of mullet 6 inches in length and a 6 inch spot fish were lowered into the pool, and the dolphins, even Albert, made mistakes.

One more test was devised by Dr. Kellogg that he might rule out even the slightest chance of any vision at all. Two fish were placed in the pool, one behind a sheet of clear glass. This could be seen if the dolphins were using vision, but naturally could not be found by sonar. In two hundred and two trials, the canny old Albert did not make a single mistake. He did not pay the least bit of attention to the fish behind the glass, but losing no time, he always assured himself of the other piece of fish. Albert was always the ever alert "smart one." His intelligence may be said to have caught even the scientists "off guard." In order to speed up

60

the experiment and get more fish Albert used a new and unusual technique. He would take his position in front of the open window even before the target fish were inserted in the water. In this advantageous position he would wait but not without exhibiting a little impatience by emitting frequent "searching" sound bursts as though scolding Dr. Kellogg for his delay. He plainly showed that he was "ready and willing" and knew precisely where to go before he had been given any reason for moving. This was an example of "anticipated action," which indicates a high degree of intelligence.

As a final, but remote, possibility, Dr. Kellogg checked against the taste or smell of the fish playing a part in its location. There was no food reward used. He placed a steel net across the pool leaving two openings; however, one was closed over by a sheet of clear glass which was alternated in position from time to time. Then the willing dolphins were chased back and forth from one end to the other. Although swimming faster than usual on account of being chased, in fifty trials they made only two errors.

Dr. Kellogg also observed the head-wagging movements. These were made only when there was noise and when there was no vision because of muddy water or darkness.

From all these experiments of about twelve years, Dr. Kellogg was able to say that the dolphin's sonar system in locating objects is 98 to 100 per cent correct.

So it has been observed by a number of scientists, and in numerous experiments, that the dolphin gives this sort of "rusty-hinge" sound that is made up of hundreds of tiny clicks or sounds, some ultrasonic, and some audible to man

61

without the use of the amplifier. These clicks or sounds, used for echo-location, bounce back when they hit an object. Then the smart old dolphin gives out these clicks again. He is sensitive to, or sure of timing. As an example, if these sounds bounce back in twelve seconds, the dolphin waits to send out more clicks until he has heard the echo from the first. Next time if his clicks come back in five seconds he knows he is getting closer to the object. Thus his timing and sonar are so perfect he locates the range accurately. Skindivers marvel at such precision.

According to Dr. Kellogg, man's ears are more intricate, yet the dolphin's ear is, as it were, insulated from sound from the surrounding flesh and bone. Sound waves travel four times faster in water than in air and there occurs much less absorption, which means that sounds also travel farther in the water.

It is a scientific fact that, by the time the air-borne sound enters the human ear, 99.9 per cent is lost by reflection. So man's ears are thus necessarily more intricate than the dolphin's.

As has been said, the sound which the dolphin answers the quickest is the splashing of a fish, or the palm of the hand on water. This is very near to the exact sound made by mullet when leaping out of the water. The dolphin soon learns this is the call to food as it is used in almost all the oceanariums. When a dolphin hears this sound, he emits those "creaking" sounds; and when "creaking," he feels sure of his aim to get a fish. When he is coming within a few feet of his target, or fish, he wags his head from side to side as though keeping time with the "creaking."

Although the dolphin may have rushed 15 feet to receive this fish, he always takes it from the human hand very gently, even softly. Mr. Gordon Kyle of Knight Key, Florida, has taught his dolphin to take fish from his mouth. The most outstanding example of the dolphin's accuracy of movement, timing, and gentleness is that of Clown, one of the show boys at The Miami Seaquarium. He leaps very high out of the water in spectacular fashion to take a cigarette very gently from the mouth of Herb Ruiz. Mr. Ruiz says he provides lip-service for Clown. Mr. Ruiz's next project is to teach Clown to smoke.

Dolphins live in a sound world much like man lives in a visual world. There are so many sounds under the water which are very important to them. For food they depend on the leaping sound of fish, the snapping little sounds of shrimp, the rolling of pebbles and sand by the tides and currents of water; the mating call; the baby and mother calling each other; the thump, thump sound of the killer whale; the intense jaw-clapping of their leader when he must lead them into deeper water to avoid the dangerous violence of a hurricane or tidal wave. Even though the dolphin's eyes are very good, many times the water is murky or muddy and the dolphin must use his excellent sonar system.

As has been said, this sonar system far exceeds anything known to man. One scientist remarked that the dolphin's sonar really makes man's system seem crude. So it is that the Navy hopes to benefit greatly from the intensive study and research on the dolphin's sonar system. Another angle of study of our dolphin friends from which the Navy expects great results, is the "why" and the "how" they gain such speed with so little output of energy. They are capable of 20 to 30 miles an hour or more.

As is known, the dolphin's skin is very smooth, elastic, and rubbery. Tests of speed with a man made model of a dolphin show that the amount of energy necessary to propel a dolphin body through the water at even 25 miles an hour, is ten times the amout of energy his muscles are able to produce. Since scientists agree that it is not probable that his muscles can produce such speed, then there surely must be some secret, or undetermined method, he has of reducing the "friction drag" of the water. This secret is the reason for the study of the speed of the dolphin in order to aid submarines and torpedoes to attain higher speeds; and it could also be used to help high-speed aircraft.

Dr. Max O. Kramer has done a great amount of careful research on this subject. He is "convinced that the dolphin has solved the problem of 'laminar flow,' which means, that, by some way, the dolphin controls the turbulence (of water) at the skin and thus reduces the 'friction drag.'" This subject becomes highly scientific; and suffice it to say in layman's terms, that the blubber which is just under the dolphin's skin is composed of a fatty, oily substance with many, many little looped blood vessels in it, the thin layer of skin being supported, as it were, by a mesh of columns. This resilient surface chokes off most of the wavelets before they break into turbulence. This is thought to be the main contributing force to the dolphin's speed. Due to its chemical substances, this blubber helps create a vacuum around the dolphin which reduces "friction drag." There is also study being given to the numerous little wrinkles in the dolphin's skin, especially on his sides, and what benefits are derived from these wrinkles.

Dr. Kramer has been instrumental in producing a synthetic dolphin skin called, "lamiflo." Our Navy and the Air Corp may gain some beneficial results by using lamiflo to cover submarines, torpedoes, missiles, and perhaps superspeed aircraft. Thus it is hoped that all can gain greatly in speed without the increase in energy.

Dr. Irving Rehman of the University of California's School of Medicine, and former Chief Consultant to the Naval Ordinance Test Station at China Lake, California, has given detailed study and thought to the speed of the dolphin. He agrees that the dolphin, in some way, controls the turbulence of water surrounding his body while swimming. This is most important because turbulent water, as has been said, gives seven times the resistance as still water to a dolphin or a submarine. Dr. Rehman says, "One reason for suspecting this as a factor in their speed is . . . unlike all other sea creatures, the porpoise (dolphin) leaves no wake in the water."

On account of the tiny looped blood vessels being close to the skin, Dr. Rehman explains, the blood vessels "liberate heat very rapidly and may serve to produce a thin layer of nonturbulent water just over the dolphin's skin. Thus the animal may actually be swimming in what amounts to be an

65

invisible envelope of nonturbulent water, or kind of vacuum, which offers only one-seventh of the normal resistance." The skin on a dolphin is seen to be loose and pliable when he is lifted. It hangs in folds and wrinkles. As a result the entire surface of a dolphin's body undulates in waves according to the waves or motion of the water. This result is known as "laminar flow," which reduces drag or friction as much as 90 per cent compared with an unyielding surface, according to Dr. Max O. Kramer's experiments. Dr. F. S. Essapian has been most successful in getting underwater pictures of this "laminar flow."

A dolphin gets three times as much power from his muscles as any other animal because his muscle cells hold a reservoir of oxygen. Also, Dr. Rehman thinks that a dolphin's method of swimming is more efficient than the propeller-power of man's inventions.

Considering these, and many other dolphin aids, the Navy has been thinking of designing ships with flexible sides, thus permitting these ships to simulate the swimming motion of the dolphin or porpoise. The dolphin's body, streamlined as it is, also helps to make it a near-perfect, drag-free contour.

The more scientific study that is made of our friends the dolphins, the more unbelievable becomes the amount they may be able to help man in his modern civilization, and — it is surely an ancient civilization in the dolphin world.

WALKING THE SHARK

When specimens are captured for the oceanariums by a specially trained crew, a great deal of patience and care is paramount. After the hardships of locating and tracing down the specimens, they must be taken without injury, and carefully and tediously placed in the holding tank of the boat without undue excitement, hurry, or harm. While in the tank they must be pampered or "nursed" along with experience and care.

Strange to say, this "babying" during capture and transportation applies more to sharks than to the smaller tropical fish. Most sharks are sensitive and shy, even reaching the point of timidity. Upon arrival at Marineland of Florida especially trained divers "walk the shark" as it is called. This is really a serious procedure by man and animal. To one not accustomed to watching it, the old shark seems downright drowsy. However, it is absolutely necessary for the sluggish or comatose shark to be moved through the water until the oxygen-bearing water, passing over his gills, revives him into activity.

A boy remarked, "And when he reached that activity stage I'd be mighty hard to catch. I'd hope for the speed of the dolphins."

A common error made by the uninformed is to mistake a swimming dolphin for a shark. The difference is easily discernable. Although a dolphin is not a porpoise, by common usage the term is often applied to dolphins. "In swimming, a porpoise 'porpoises'; that is, its fin (triangular dorsal) goes up and down rhythmically as it comes up to breathe. A shark will never porpoise, and its fin, when out of the water, remains in the same horizontal plane."

Sharks, porpoises, and dolphins can be kept in the same tank so far as the shark bothering any of the dwellers is concerned, but dolphins and porpoises tease sharks so much that it shortens their lives in captivity.

Zippy

ZIPPY AND ELVAR ARE TWO of the best known living dolphins contributing of their knowledge, energy, and patience to the fascinating scientific studies for the benefit of mankind. Elvar definitely "belongs" and is wrapped up in all of Dr. John C. Lilly's work in the field of dolphin communication.

Now Zippy "belongs," in somewhat the same way, to Dr. Kenneth S. Norris, well-known author and curator at Marineland of the Pacific. Although Dr. Norris is only in his late thirties, he is ten times older than Zippy; yet this youngster of a dolphin has "taught him a lot." Dr. Norris prefers young animals for his experiments. He says, after all, "They're much more adaptable than the old folks."

Zippy is a slender bottle-nosed dolphin, 5 feet 2 inches in length, weighing only three hundred pounds, and possess-

69

ing dazzling speed. She is smart and, according to scientific dolphin standards, possesses intelligence to a marked degree. She is emotional but never to the point where it would hinder her good disposition or willingness to co-operate. She most assuredly has a sense of humor and at times is a real little prankster.

Mr. Wesley Griswold, in writing the story of Zippy's life for *Popular Science,* says she "can do a lot of astonishing tricks. Her voice would break your heart, though. When she is invited to sing she sounds like a terrified baby." However, her contribution to scientific knowledge dims her other accomplishments. She is really known as, "The Blindfolded Dolphin." She swims through a man made tank as readily and as accurately as a well directed torpedo, although she is wearing rubber cups over her eyes.

For quite some time scientists have been experimenting, feeling certain that dolphins, porpoises, and whales have built-in sonar systems. So it is that these "Norris-Zippy workouts" have, as Dr. Norris explained, "put the finishing, conclusive touches on these experiments concerning sonar." Many of these had been carried out earlier by Dr. William Schevill and his wife, Barbara, who have made significant contributions to science, especially in this sonar field. Their work is done at the Oceanograpic Institute at Woods Hole, Massachusetts. Dr. Winthrop Kellogg, of Florida State University, has done a great amount of research and contributed valuable information and results in this same field. He is the author of several impressive and helpful books on this subject.

After all of this conclusive research that had gone on before, there were still several points that Dr. Norris wanted to clear in his own mind. One was how much, if any, had these dolphins depended on their excellent vision, although some of the experiments had been carried out at night and in muddy water. He decided to blindfold a dolphin, and here is where Zippy entered the picture. She was brought to California from Marine Studios or Marineland of Florida in St. Augustine, Florida, by plane and suspended on a stretcher while the blanket over her was kept wet. Although she had received a kindergarten education in Florida, four months of daily sessions were required before she would allow herself to be blindfolded. After all, wearing "blinkers" was something new in the life history of dolphins.

From the very first, Zippy captured the hearts of her trainers and especially of Dr. Norris. They used patience, tenderness, and love. She was deprived of food, as is the usual procedure, until she would allow the men to touch her. She was very fidgety when they started the first steps toward the blindfolding — namely, cupping their hands over her eyes. Finally she agreed to the cupped hands. The next question was what type of blinkers would they use. They tried wearing gloves to accustom her to the touch of something other than their hands. She did not approve of the gloves but submitted after some coaxing.

Mr. Griswold tells of the last tedious steps as Dr. Norris related them to him. Next, "We tried ear-muffs on a head-band. That was a great mistake. The headband came too close to her nostril — the blowhole — and she refused to

71

breathe. We couldn't let her suffocate for science, so we gave up that approach." Finally rubber suction cups were the perfect solution. She allowed them to remain over her eyes the very first time.

Zippy had been taught, before being blindfolded, to swim across the tank at the sound of a whistle and to press a button which rang a bell. So with the above preparations completed, one of the big moments of this experiment was at hand. With blinkers effectively blinding her, Dr. Norris very quietly changed the location of the button. Then he blew the whistle as usual. "Zippy charged forward, moving her blinded head from side to side, as if she were signaling, 'No.' Hydrophones recorded a storm of rusty-hinge sounds. Though she was obviously searching with her sonar, there was hardly an instant's hesitation before she swam straight up to the target and gave it a bold, triumphant nudge."

This experiment was successfully accomplished again and again. The size of the target was gradually reduced until it was only an inch in diameter. Zippy was still the perfect marksman swimming from 35 feet away from the target. Her sonar-aim was 100 per cent perfect. Dr. Norris used this experiment to prove other facts. He also covered Zippy's tiny little ear holes (canals) with foam rubber suction cups. Now she was blind and deaf. Her aim was just as perfect.

These experiments were enlarged upon. Dr. Norris found that Zippy could not find food placed below the level of her nose no matter how close she was to it. If above the nose she never missed; therefore Dr. Norris was sure that a dolphin's sonar machinery must be above his throat. The hydrophones sounded with their greatest intensity just above her head and in front of her nose. This gave Dr. Norris the idea of making a foam rubber mask to fit over Zippy's snout and the front portion of her head. If, as he thought, the sonar transmissions or echo-locations came from her snout and head, then this mask would cut off her sonar system.

Right here Zippy decided a few things for herself. She absolutely and unequivocally refused to wear the mask. The men were successful in slipping it over her face a few times, but only for an instant at a time. She would back away at once and shake her head violently until the mask bounced off into the water. Zippy would not enjoy a halloween party, for the men tried three months to get her to wear the mask; they finally gave in to a determined little Zippy.

Mr. Griswold wrote, "But Zippy wanted them to know that though nobody could make a fool of her, she was not one to bear a grudge. Each time she shook off the mask she picked it up in her teeth and obligingly brought it back to her tormenters."

Dr. Kenneth Norris, Professor of Zoology at U.C.L.A., California, speaks of dolphins with enthusiasm and great admiration — even love — when he says, "really like people, bless 'em."

Carolina Snowball

NOT FOR A DAY, BUT queen for as long as she lives, is a fairly safe prediction to make for Carolina Snowball. Fact, not fancy, reigns in the story of this albino dolphin.

To quote from Jane Wood of the Hank Meyer Associates in her article, "Carolina Snowball": "Moby Dick, re-written as a comedy by ocean-going hunters of the Miami Seaquarium, became one of the twentieth century's great sagas of the sea in the summer of 1962.

"Melville's nineteenth century tragedy told the story of mad, peg-legged Captain Ahab and his pursuit of Moby Dick, the great white whale that took him to his death.

"The Seaquarium version differs from Melville's tragedy in that it has a happy ending and in other ways. There were two Captain Ahabs heading this chase, Captain Bill Gray and Captain Emil Hansen. Neither has a peg-leg. Neither is mad. The white whale is pint-sized, and really pale pink

75

— a bottle-nosed dolphin named Carolina Snowball. Snowball is a beautiful, friendly, kind, smart little lady cousin of the whales, not a cruel, mean, old whale.

"But the splendid audacity of both cases was equal."

Word reached the Miami Seaquarium of Florida that a white dolphin had been seen on occasions streaking through the waters of Helena Sound, South Carolina. Was this an apparition of beauty, a ghost of the dolphin world, or was this beauty a tantalizing reality?

There have been very few reports through the ages of white dolphins or of white whales being seen anywhere. Was this one of those miracle appearances right here on our own shores? Such a story was worth immediate investigation.

Captain Hansen of the Seaquarium collecting vessel, Captain Gray, Director of the Seaquarium, and Mr. Burton Clark, Seaquarium Manager, decided that the present was the time for action. For three weeks these two captains searched the waters by day and night for this reported beauty. The moment came and they dropped the net over her. She sneaked from under the net as easily as an old escape artist. Was she a ghost or was she real? Her escape seemed phantom-like. She had eluded these experienced captains without effort. Her escape only served to make her pursuers more determined. In January 1962, they almost had this wily beauty as their prize — then she broke the net.

This white dolphin had been sighted many times by the commercial fishermen of Beaufort County. However, few other people had actually seen her. No sensational interest

76

was aroused until word leaked out that the beauty was being pursued by the captains of the Miami Seaquarium. As Miss Wood reminds us, it is the same old story of "the girl next door." No one had courted or paid attention to her until she was considered a beauty and was highly desirable to the Seaquarium.

Immediately legal fever-heat was engendered. A law was passed in Beaufort County, South Carolina, which made it illegal to net porpoises in said county, which county includes part of the waters of Helena Sound. Later, in April, the South Carolina legislature passed, "An act making it unlawful to net, trap, harpoon, lasso, or molest genus Delphinis or genus Tursiops in the waters of Beaufort County." The scientific specie or name of Carolina Snowball is Tursiops truncatus.

Now the pursuing captains, still undaunted, had to be very careful. With a new net and a vast amount of determination, they embarked on a third sea hunt for this "Southern Beauty." They cruised in the waters of Collecton Bay where no law had been passed concerning the capture of dolphins. Dame Fortune followed them, and they carefully dropped their net around the prize white dolphin and her little dark baby boy whom they called, "Sonny Boy." The dolphins were gently and easily lifted aboard the ship into its center water tank or pool, and they were hurriedly shipped to Miami.

The people of South Carolina accused the captains of Miami Seaquarium of "porpoise-poaching, porpoise piracy and porpoise-napping." Mr. Burton Clark answered their

77

wails with facts, namely, that the white porpoise, now named Carolina Snowball, would be far happier in her elaborate new home than in the silt-laden Helena Sound, and that she would have excellent care and the best of everything that a dolphin's heart could desire — and no more fears on her part of killer whales, sharks, or fishermen's nets.

The South Carolina State Senator, James M. Waddell Jr., who authored and introduced the bill making porpoise netting illegal in Beaufort County, said: "If Snowball cavorted out of Beaufort County, she had no legal protection. If the fickle vixen had just stayed in Beaufort water, she'd be swimming there now."

Snowball received a whale-sized welcome when she arrived in her large new pool in the Seaquarium. Writers grew lyrical and wrote of "the showery flip of her rare pale tail." A few of the editorials written about these dolphins, quoted in Jane Wood's article, make most interesting quotes: "Sonny Boy. . . . product of his mother's union with a normal dark porpoise, . . . swam with her close as a black piano key to white." A reporter said, "The kidnapping of Carolina Snowball is a clear-cut violation of the porpoise's civil rights. But what good are states' or civil rights if they don't serve a useful porpoise?" A typical Floridian reply to the above editorial "Snowball in the Sun" was "White porpoises prefer Florida two to one. Our mammal's done told us."

Carolina Snowball measures eight feet in length and weighs four hundred pounds. Her age is estimated at ten years. Being a true albino with no pigment in her skin, it is

78

entirely possible that she is the only such animal in existence. It is possible that others have been born, but experience with albinism in wild creatures indicates they seldom reach maturity.

Carolina Snowball's baby, Sonny Boy, swims quite close to his mother, very sure of her protection. He is of normal color, appears to be between eighteen months and two years of age (this was at the time of capture). It is assumed he was born to the white dolphin or else there is a plain case of kid-napping or dolphin-napping.

In her wild state Carolina Snowball was vulnerable to many natural enemies, particularly the vicious sand tiger sharks which are especially numerous off the coast of the Middle Atlantic States. She was exposed to possible harpooning or shooting by many persons who might consider this quite a feat. This danger has increased in recent years because of heavy traffic on the Intercoastal Waterway.

Today, Carolina Snowball, perhaps in the wisdom that is a dolphin's, is cognizant of the fact that she is living happily as the only white bottle-nosed dolphin in any aquarium on the earth. Since albinos in any specie of the animal kingdom are very rare, she is being carefully watched. Tape recordings and studies are made of her "conversation" to add to man's knowledge of albinos and dolphinese. Since her eyes are void of pigment, she holds them half-closed in a coquettish, winking pose to protect them from the light; this impish pose, along with the natural smile that bottle-nosed dolphins possess, make her irresistible.

Captain Gray says of Carolina Snowball, "She is the smartest personal porpoise friend I have ever had, black or white, and in my career of over fifty years as a sea-hunter I have known hundreds of the fleet, sweet creatures."

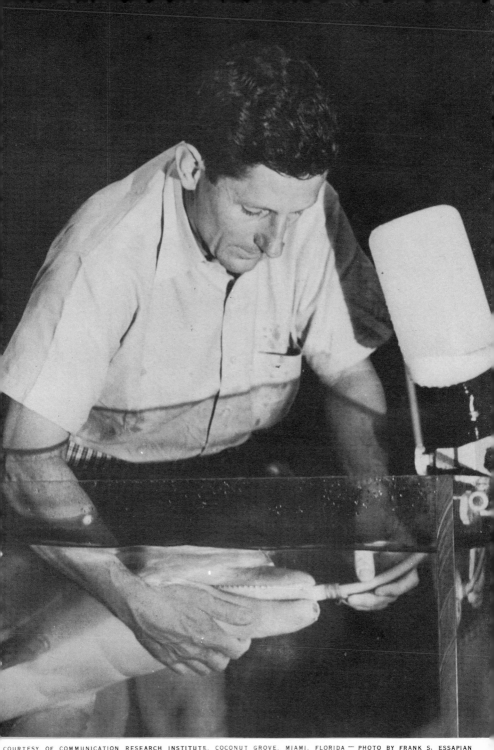

r. John C. Lilly watches a baby dolphin wrap its tongue around tube, sealing out salt water.

A scientific investigator swims with a dolphin to become acquainted with air breathing mamm

Clown laughing with inner tube on snout.

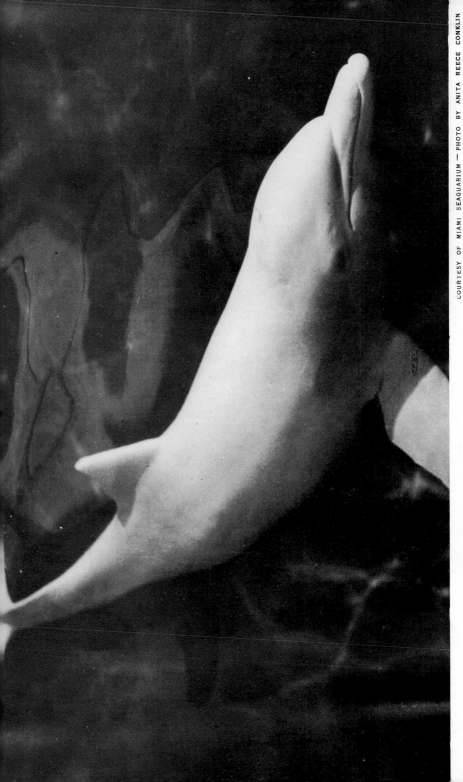

Carolina Snowball, the world's only known albino dolphin, was captured off the Carolina coast.

Carolina Snowball, the rare and beautiful albino porpoise, says "hi!"

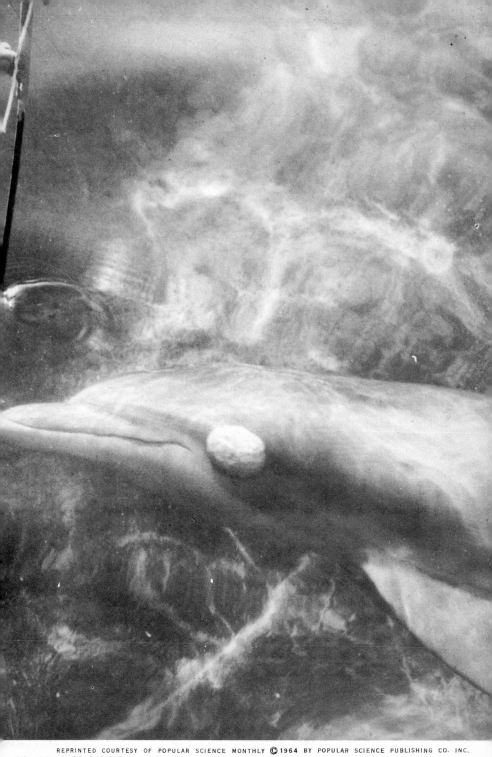

The blindfolded dolphin proves his excellent sonar system is not related to his vision.

The dolphin leaps many feet to receive his reward for a job well done.

Opo

No book on dolphins would be complete without the factual story about Opo, told by the able writer Anthony Alpers.

EARLY IN 1955 IN THE SMALL TOWN OF Opononi, on the western side of the North Island of New Zealand, boat owners of Hokianga Harbour noticed a dolphin following their boats. The sound of a motor seemed to attract Opo (that was the name given her), and she would follow along like a dog. She played around near shore and always seemed happiest when there were many people nearby. She was so playful and friendly that people came just to see her. Her fame spread, and children begged to go watch Opo. On Saturdays and Sundays the roads were crowded. Stores had excellent business. The beach was lined with onlookers. Tents were pitched for great distances up and down the beach. People were always in a holiday mood. Those who had been strangers an hour before were visiting each other in their tents.

Many swam and played in the water. Some became so excited when Opo was seen that they waded out to get a better look, seeming to forget that they were fully clothed. Opo loved children, and she would swim up close to them as though wanting to be petted.

Jill Baker, a thirteen-year-old girl who lived on the main road by the beach, was an experienced and adept swimmer and was in the water at every opportunity. Opo became very fond of Jill and would come on the gallop whenever she heard or saw Jill come into the water. Jill was always very easy and quiet in her manner with Opo and never rushed at her as others did. Opo wanted Jill to pet her and would rub against Jill. Soon she would go very carefully between Jill's legs and taking her on her back would treat Jill to a nice ride, never carrying her out to deep water. She would also allow Jill to put small children on her back for short rides.

Jill gave Opo a large, brightly colored beach ball. She soon learned to toss it high over her head with her snout. Then she would race to catch it as it came down. She loved for Jill to race with her and looked ever so happy when she was ahead of Jill and got the ball. Then she learned to press the ball way down under the water, let it go, and then race to get under it as it bounced high in the air when it escaped from under the water. She learned to toss the ball in the air, and, with the greatest agility and swiftness, hit it with her

82

tail. Some of the boys said she was playing baseball using her tail at a bat.

Opo loved an audience, and whenever she received applause she would give an exultant leap in the air, but never close enough to harm any bathers. One of her most laughable stunts was the manner she had of teasing photographers who tried to take her picture. She would push herself to the bottom of the bay and then try to lift them off their feet with her snout. When people were rough with her or tried to hold her flippers, she would swim away, splashing her tail in the water to show her annoyance.

Crowds continued to grow; they would talk, visit, and the children would play. "There was such an overflow of these friendly feelings that it seemed the crowds were composed of people wanting to be forgiven for something — for the unkindness, perhaps, that humans generally do to animals in the wild. The dolphin, who never once snapped at a hand, seemed to offer forgiveness for all."

Opo was given the same protection by law that Pelorus Jack had enjoyed. This legal pronouncement of her protection read, "By order of the Council made in the presence of the Governor-General. These regulations were gazetted on Thursday, March 8, 1956 and they became law at 12 o'clock that night."

It has always seemed strange that on that very day, Thursday, Opo failed to appear in her usual happy way. She was there only the day before and had played with the children and bathers. Some fishermen had also seen her in the morning. That afternoon a motor boat went out to get her, as a photographer had come to take pictures of her. She loved the sound of a motor and would always come at once. But she did not come and could not be found. Once or twice before she had been gone for twenty-four hours; but on Friday when she failed to appear, four boats went out to search for her. At noon an old fisherman found her dead body. It was pushed into a crevice between some rocks at Kouter Point about 5 miles up from the harbour. Evidently she had been feeding there, and when the tide went out, she was left trapped in a small pool. The crevice was her only escape and signs showed that she had tried to squeeze through.

A gloom settled over the village of Opononi when news of her death came. She was buried by the side of Memorial Hall, and over her grave there were masses of flowers. When told of her death, children cried; a girls' hockey team came onto the field wearing black mourning bands. Telegrams were sent to the village from all parts of the world expressing sympathy. A telegram also came from the Governor-General. A message of sympathy was sent by Sir Willoughby Norris from the Government House.

The words the classical poet, Oppian, wrote of the dolphin were true of Opo, "Excellence and majesty attend them even when they perish, nor do they shame their glory even when they die."

Bibliography

BOOKS

Alpers, Antony. *Dolphins, The Myth and The Mammal.* Boston: Houghton Mifflin Co.; Cambridge: The Riverside Press. Copyright by Antony Alpers, 1961.

Brothers, Betty. *RA — OO and the Porpoise.* Coral Gables, Florida: Wake-Brook House. Copyright by Betty Miller Brothers, 1962.

Chapin, Henry. *The Remarkable Dolphin.* New York: William R. Scott Inc., 1962.

Clarke, Arthur C. *Dolphin Island.* New York: Holt, Rinehart, and Winston, 1963.

Drimmer, Frederick. *The Animal Kingdom.* Garden City Books: Doubleday & Company Inc., 1954. "The Frozen Smile" — Dolphin.

Gray, Captain William B. *Creatures of the Sea.* New York: Wilford Funk Inc. Copyright by William B. Gray, 1960.

85

Kay, Helen. *The Secrets of the Dolphin.* New York: Macmillan Co. Copyright by Helen Kay, 1964.

Kellogg, Winthrop N. *Porpoises and Sonar.* Chicago: The University of Chicago Press, 1961.

Lilly, John C. *Man and Dolphin.* Copyright by John C. Lilly, 1961. Reprinted by permission of Doubleday & Company Inc.

MAGAZINE ARTICLES

Andrew, R. J. "Evolution of Intelligence and Vocal Mimicking," *Science,* CXXXVII, No. 3530 (August 24, 1962), 585-9.

Appel, Frederick C. "The Intellectual Mammal," New Status Symbol, *The Saturday Evening Post,* CCXXXVII (January 4, 1962), 22-32.

Cohen, Daniel. "Porpoise Rated Genius Among Animals," *Science Digest,* XLVIII, No. 1 (July 1, 1960), 47. From *National Geographic News Bulletin,* February 5, 1960.

Cohen, Daniel. "Smarty of the Sea," *Science Digest,* XLVIII, No. 6 (December, 1960), 4307.

Clarke, Arthur C. *Scientific American* (March, 1960).

"Clever Innovaters," (Dolphins Hitch Free Rides on Bow Waves of Ships), *News Letter,* LXXV (May 2, 1959), 278. Observations of Dr. Scholander of Scripps Institute of Oceanography.

Dufresne, Frank. "Fly on the Ocean," *Field and Stream,* LXVIII (August, 1963), 34-5.

Edwards, Robert L. and Livingston Jr., Robert. "Observations on Behavior," *Science*, CXXXII, No. 3418 (July 1, 1960), 35.

"Gaining Recognition As a Mental Giant in the Animal Kingdom," *National Geographic News Bulletin*, National Geographic Society, Washington D. C. (February 5, 1960).

Griswold, Wesley. "The Case of the Blindfolded Dolphin," *Popular Science*, CLXXVII (August, 1960), 70-3. Reprinted courtesy *Popular Science Monthly* (c) by Popular Science Publishing Company, Inc.

Lilly, John C. and Miller, A. M. "Vocal Exchange Between Dolphins," *Science*, CXXXIV, No. 3493 (December 8, 1961), 1873-6.

Lilly, John C. "Where Is Science Taking Us," *Saturday Review*, XLIV (October 7, 1961), 58-9.

O'Reilly, J. and Brothers, Berm. "A Pet Porpoise in a Pool," *Sports Illustrated*, XIX (September 23, 1963), 81-2.

Peterson, R. F. "Thar What Blows," *Yatching*, III, No. 2 (February, 1962), 60-1.

Poling, James. "Egghead — Clown of the Sea," *Coronet*, XLIX (April, 1961), 50-4.

Scott, Jack Denton. "Brainy Prankster of the Sea," *Reader's Digest*, LXXX (February, 1962), 166. (Condensed from *Audubon.)*

Scott, Jack Denton. "That Remarkable Animal, the Porpoise," *Audubon Magazine*, LXIV (January, 1962), 30-1.

Tomkins, Calvin. "Conversation at Sea Level," *The New Yorker*, XXXVI (September 3, 1960), 24-6.

Waters, Harry. "Five Beeps and a Tweet" — System of Inter-
    species Communication, *Newsweek,* LX (October 22,
    1962), 83.

NEWSPAPER ARTICLES

Dighton, Ralph. "Navy's Porpoise for Tests: What Makes
    Sonar Click?" *The Miami Herald* (July 16, 1964).
Kelly, Brian. "Flipper," (TV Show), Waco *Tribune Herald*
    (August 30, 1964).
Plain, Carl. "Lockheed Dolphin Studies Revealing," *The
    San Diego Union* (California) (May 19, 1964).

BROCHURES AND LEAFLETS

Dr. John C. Lilly, Miami, Florida.
Dr. Winthrop N. Kellogg, Florida State University, Talla-
    hassee, Florida and Stanford Research Institute, Menlo
    Park, California.
Florida Development Commission, Tallahassee, Florida.
Hank Meyer Associates Inc., Miami Beach, Florida. "Caro-
    lina Snowball," by Jane Wood.
Marineland of Florida, St. Augustine, Florida.
Marineland of the Pacific, Palos Verdes Estates, California.
Seaquarium, Miami, Florida.
Sea World, San Diego, California.
United States Government, Washington D.C.

Index

91

Initiative, 19
Inner tube, 21
Instinct, 44
Intelligence, 17-19, 23, 26, 28, 35, 37, 45, 50, 53, 58-61, 70
Intercoastal Waterway, 79
Inventiveness, 17
Island of St. Croix, 56

J

Jaw, 13-14, 49, 63
Joy, 24, 36
Kay, Helen, 86
Kazan, Dr. B., 29, 38
Kellogg, Dr. Winthrop N., 29, 58-62, 70, 86, 88
Kelly, Brian, 88
Kipling, Rudyard, 2
Knight Key, Florida, 63
Kouter Point, 84
Kramer, Dr. Max O., 64-66
Kyle, Gordon, 63

L

Lamiflo, 65
Laminar flow, 28, 64, 66
Languages, 11, 28-29, 39, 48-49, 51-52, 56, 58
Larynx, 53
Laws for dolphins, 2, 4, 77-78, 83
Law suits, 33
Leader, 13, 26
Legs, 12-13, 82
Library of Congress, 56
Life Science, 28
Lilly, Dr. John C., 29, 37-38, 48-56, 69, 86-88
Lips, 13, 18, 53
Liver, 14
Livingston, Robert Jr., 86
Lockheed Aircraft Corporation, 27-28
Locomotion, 16
Loneliness, 52-53
Longevity, 31-33, 35
Love, 10-11, 35, 44, 55, 71, 73
Lungs, 14-15

M

MGM, 36
Man and Dolphin, 86
Marineland of Florida, 10, 20, 23, 35, 41-42, 67, 71, 77, 88; *See also* Miami Seaquarium
Marineland of the Pacific, 23-25 27, 37-38, 69, 88
Marine schools, 22
Marine Studios, 59, 71
Marlborough Express, 4
Mask, 73
Maturity, 35
Melville, 75
Memory, 17
Mexican Indians, 39
Meyer Associates, Inc., 75, 78, 88; *See also* Hank Meyer Associates Inc.
Miami Seaquarium, 10, 23, 44, 63, 75-78, 88; *See also* Marineland of Florida
Middle Atlantic States, 79
Milk of the dolphins, 41-42
Miller, A.M., 87
Mimic, 50-51, 54
Missiles, 65
Mitzi, 36
Moby Dick, 75
Morrison, Bill, 4
Mother dolphins, 41-44
Mother love, 43-44
Motion picture, 37
Mouth, 9, 13-14, 21, 35, 41, 63
Moving head, 59, 72; *See also* Head wagging
Muscles, 12, 16, 28, 32, 41, 64, 66
Music, 2, 25, 39
Musketeers, 22

N

NBC, 36
National defense, 58
National Geographic Society, 17
National History, 25
Naval Research, 27, 58, 63-66
Navigation, 27, 50, 58, 60
Nelson, 2
Nelson Run, 3
Nervous system, 11, 28, 49

94

V

Vacuum, 65-66
Variety in training, 55
Vertebrae, 13
Virgin Islands, 56
Vision, 14, 58, 60-61, 71
Vocabulary, 39
Vocalizing, 25, 50-53, 55
Voice, 53, 70

W

Waddell, James M. Jr., State Senator, 78
Wagging head, 63; *See also* Moving head
Wake in the water, 65
Walking the shark, 67
Warning signal, 26
War, 47
Water fowl, 43
Water organ, 25

Water polo, 39
Waters, Harry, 88
Wave good-bye, 24, 26
Weightlessness, 47-48
Wellington, 2, 4
Whale, 7-8, 13-14, 23-24, 28, 38, 63, 70, 76, 78
Whistle, 37, 39, 50, 53
Whale and Dolphin College, 38
Willingness, 26, 28, 32, 70
Wine, 32
Wood, Jane, 75, 77-78
Woods Hole, Mass., 70
World War II, 45
Wrinkles, 65-66
Write, 38
Wrist, 12

Z

Zippy, 69, 71-73
Zoology, 47